I DIDN'T SIGN UP FOR THIS SHIT

I DIDN'T SIGN UP FOR THIS SHIT

A Book About Love and Hope

MICHAEL R. LEWIS, MD

Books may be purchased by visiting the publisher and author at: www.michaellewismd.com or www.willowbaypress.com

Cover Design: Willow Bay Press

Editing and Interior Design: Kate Winter

Line Editing: Dr. Jenniffer Lewis, Ph.D.

ISBN: 978-0-578-27040-1

Library of Congress Control Number: 2022915711

First Edition

Printed in the United States of America

To my wife, Jenn:
Now, this is the shit I signed up for!
You are my favorite person.

Contents

A Quick Note to the Reader

Though I refer primarily to physicians in this book, it was not meant to be exclusionary. The word *physician* can be substituted with *provider, clinician, advanced practice practitioner, physician assistant, nurse practitioner, nurse, or anyone who sees patients.* However, there are some instances where I am speaking directly to a doctor (MD or DO) because of our unique experiences or scope of practice.

The terms *insurance-based* and *traditional* model of medicine can be interchanged.

Though I discuss some specific topics about health insurance, I am not an expert. I paint some ideas with broad brush strokes to illustrate my point of view. These are my opinions and experiences that I've had and not meant to be an exhaustive diatribe on the health insurance company business model.

This book is unique because it is a *manual*, a *memoir*, and a *rant*. The *manual* piece is peppered throughout the entire book and was initially written to strengthen my points of view or arguments. However, as the book developed, I connected to some powerful insights. The *memoir* piece is, of course, weaved in and out of this book and spoken through true stories of interactions that I've had with patients, staff, and other healthcare providers. The *rant* parts are placed strategically within certain sections and have a specific tone—you won't miss them.

A major topic in the book is mental health because it's so prevalent in our practices as primary care providers. I think healthcare providers can do a better job in this area.

I do my best to recollect and write stories/anecdotes as they *actually* happened. As I've matured and recall how I handled some situations, there were some that I would have handled differently. When appropriate, I illustrate up-to-date examples. Otherwise, I just left them as they were.

Preface

It's June 16, 2022, and I'm sitting in the Hassler Hotel in Rome, Italy, reflecting on the journey of writing this book. Coincidentally, I began writing this book seven years ago, on July 5, 2015, on an earlier trip to Rome. On that flight, I wrote the table of contents and outline. However, the book remained dormant for the next year and a half before I would type the first sentence. As I was falling asleep the other night thinking about writing this preface, I realized that this book was almost 20 years in the making. Holy shit, where did the time go? This journey has been an incredible and life-changing evolution, both personally and professionally.

If you would've asked me when I was 24 what I thought my life would look like at 47, I don't think I could've imagined the twists and turns it took. The day after my Bar Mitzvah, I bought my first guitar. Music became my passion, my calling. Little did I know that a conversation during an organic chemistry group study break would change me forever.

I said, "You know, I think I wanna become a doctor." My study partner's book slammed, and he swiveled towards me on the brown recliner he was sitting on. "Mike, you know, if you wanna do this, you need to make some sacrifices. Stop going out every weekend. Stay in and study. Put down your guitar, man." I thought, "I can do that . . . but put down my guitar?!" Over the next week, I felt the grief of losing my dream of becoming a professional musician. A week later, I told my mom and my best friend at the time, "I'm done screwing around. I'm going to be a doctor." On the next organic chemistry test, I earned an A—the first of my college career. From then on, I was unstoppable. Almost every grade I earned from then on out was an A. Once I found my stride, I found my guitar again.

Caring for patients as a phlebotomist, an EMT (Emergency Medical Technician), a medical student, a first-year medical resident, a new attending, and a senior attending/supervising physician, the one consistent thought that ran through my mind was, "What the hell is wrong with our system and our healthcare professionals?" I've witnessed doctors treating medical students as if they were beneath them, patients treated as a cluster of symptoms, and corporate medicine masquerading as high-quality patient care—the ultimate wolf in sheep's clothing.

It's tricky being an employee in corporate medicine. Many times, I've had the desire to be a whistle blower, to speak up and risk being fired. But there's no whistle to blow because nothing I'm discussing is illegal; it's just bad practice. Now I'm free. Free from the bureaucratic grip squeezing me into submission and manipulating my practice of medicine. Regardless, I am grateful for the roads and paths I took to arrive where I am today.

If, during or after reading this book, you share similar experiences, maybe this book will help you cope, realize you're not alone, help you move through your insecurities and fears, or, most importantly, find your voice.

Please enjoy this book.

The Modern Hippocratic Oath

I swear to fulfill, to the best of my ability and judgment, this covenant:

I will do no harm.

I will respect the hard-won scientific gains of those physicians in whose steps I walk, and gladly share such knowledge as is mine with those who are to follow.

I will apply, for the benefit of the sick, all measures which are required, avoiding those twin traps of overtreatment and therapeutic nihilism.

I will remember that there is art to medicine as well as science, and that warmth, sympathy, and understanding may outweigh the surgeon's knife or the chemist's drug.

I will not be ashamed to say, "I know not," nor will I fail to call in my colleagues when the skills of another are needed for a patient's recovery.

I will respect the privacy of my patients. Most especially, tread with care in matters of life and death. Above all, I must not play at God.

I will remember that I do not treat a fever chart, a cancerous growth, but a sick human being, whose illness may affect the person's family and economic stability. My responsibility includes these related problems, if I am to care adequately for the sick.

I will prevent disease whenever I can, for prevention is preferable to cure.

I will remember that I remain a member of society, with special obligations to all my fellow human beings, those sound of mind and body as well as the infirm.

If I do not violate this oath, may I enjoy life and art, respected while I live and remembered with affection thereafter. May I always act so as to preserve the finest traditions of my calling, and may I long experience the joy of healing those who seek my help.

PART
ONE

WHY I'M WRITING THIS BOOK

The Kiss That Changed Everything

"Pull a thread here and you'll find it's attached to the rest of the world."

— Nadeem Aslam, *The Wasted Vigil*

I WAS A SECOND-YEAR MEDICAL STUDENT when I stepped into the local emergency room. It wasn't to see a patient but to see my Bubby (Yiddish for grandma). Pauline was 92 years old, in the last days of her life. She arrived at the hospital with a diagnosis of "Altered Level of Consciousness," exacerbated by a sleep medication she had taken the night before. I walked into the ER and headed directly to her room, where she was lying unresponsive but alive. My family was gathered around her hospital bed telling stories, laughing, crying, and sitting with the painful realization that she would die tonight. I sat with her and wondered if there was something I could offer to reverse her current state, given my newly found "expertise" as a medical student who had just finished pharmacology. I remembered the proper antidote to counteract the effects of the benzodiazepine she took the night prior. I offered it up to the doctor who was caring for her, and he was nice enough to hear me and thought it was a good idea. Shortly after, the nurse came in with a syringe filled with the medicine and pushed it into her IV. Initially, there was a small, hopeful response, but not much. It was time to accept that my Bubby was on her way out of this world.

We all gathered around her as she took her last breaths. We wept over her dying body. The monitor showed asystole (flatline), and she passed on. (Side note: In medicine, the patient isn't *legally* dead until a doctor makes the final confirmation.)

Within a couple of minutes, a different doctor walked in. She stood at the foot of the bed as she gave her condolences. Her eyes were honest and revealed authentic compassion during this profound moment. She explained that she had to officially "pronounce" my Bubby dead. The doctor walked over to her left side, listened to her heart and lungs, and looked at her pupils. It was official. The doctor put her right hand on Bubby's forehead and bowed her head in silence. She got very close, whispered, "Rest in peace," and kissed her forehead. I was moved. I thought, "Who does this?" She was a true healer.

That moment remains ingrained in my mind. I will never forget how special it was that this emergency room physician, who sees death every day, would give a stranger this sincere gesture of love.

I learned from this moment that the doctor-patient relationship must stand tantamount to the knowledge of medicine itself. At the same time, a more profound connection is necessary for healing beyond the physical.

To date, I can't remember how many foreheads I've kissed, but it's been plenty.

CLOSENESS IN PRIMARY CARE

"If fear is the great enemy of intimacy, love is its true friend."

— Henri Nouwen

AS I TRANSITIONED INTO BEING A PHYSICIAN, I realized one major thing: The relationship is at least as vital as the healing process itself. What is healing? I believe healing is the alleviation of discomfort in both the physical and the emotional aspects of the individual. Of course, physical, or emotional healing can exist individually, but in many cases, there is significant overlap. Trust and rapport are crucial when facilitating a healing process, especially when the patient is coming in for a separate issue all together (at least in their eyes). This trust and rapport sets the foundation for more authentic sharing:

Maria M. was a 53-year-old female with chronic, poorly-controlled Type II Diabetes Mellitus. She was overweight and didn't exercise. She was taking three medications to control her blood sugar. We had spent years trying to sort out her sugars, but despite education, diet discussions, frequent visits, and food journaling, she still had very poor control. She struggled with her diet, culturally, bread and rice were staples in her kitchen. One afternoon she came to see me. I looked at her recent labs, which were worse than ever. Her hemoglobin A1c (a measure of someone's blood sugar control) was 10.2%. The accepted normal is less than 6.5%. I asked her about diet, exercise, etc., but she fell back on the excuse of, "It's hard . . . I don't have time." "I get it," I thought, so I switched gears. I asked her, "What's really going on, Maria? I see you struggling here. I wonder what's getting in the way of you caring about yourself enough to make a change." She sat there for a moment, somewhat bewildered by my comment, and then began to cry. I listened as she told me about the issues that were troubling her. Before we ended, we embraced. I validated her feelings while normalizing her suffering. But for how long would she let these feelings control her? She felt a little better, and we ended the meeting. I saw her shortly after, and she started to make changes because she knew she was sabotaging herself. We discussed seeing a therapist to assist her with these normal and intrusive feelings.

CONNECTION IS MORE THAN A TRANSACTION

"I exist in two places, here and where you are."

— Margaret Atwood

IF YOU TOOK YOUR CAR TO THE MECHANIC and they fixed the dents and scratches but forgot to top off your fluids and put air in your tires, would you be satisfied? I believe physicians need to start looking deeper than just the exterior to encourage deeper healing. What's the difference between a doctor who can't connect to their patient and a robot?

Nothing.

As physicians, we need to step out of robotic interactions and connect to the person in front of us to see beyond just their chief complaints. The *ability* to connect with our patients is one of the most vital elements in our arsenal because, without it, we miss a substantial opportunity for deeper healing.

Shy and introverted, doctors can provide good medicine for many things. However, they may struggle when handling issues which require a deeper understanding of the patient's psyche. They may have more trouble active listening and asking meaningful questions, which usually go much further than a prescription for *Prozac*. Many doctors would retort, "Who has time for that?" Or "I only have seven minutes to see my patients." This is a pervasive, multifactorial problem that will be discussed throughout this book.

Regardless of time, if providers don't invite more meaningful conversation, can they *really* know what's going on? The relationships we have with our patients are a privilege and should be thought of as such. I have been privileged enough, just as many of you, to sit across from emotionally suffering patients who have allowed me to be their confidant. They've shared things with me that even their spouse or partner does not know. They trusted me enough to reveal the most intimate aspects of their life because I cared enough to ask and, more importantly, listen. Instead of feeling drained or burdened, I would leave these interactions feeling inspired and rejuvenated. As we move through this book, we will also see how a physician's issues may interfere with trust and rapport in the doctor-patient relationship. For example, suppose you have trouble letting people get close or feel uncomfortable with showing emotions. In that case, you will no doubt have a more challenging time developing a meaningful relationship with your patient (not to mention with your partner or spouse). This may be an important realization for you. It's nice to see the areas where there's a growth opportunity.

Over the years, I've found that people have similar wants and desires. Knowing this makes it possible to connect to patients almost instantly. I've found through my experiences, especially working in fast-paced urgent care centers, that it's the quality of the connection that's most important.

WE ARE COMPLEX BEINGS

"For a man to conquer himself is the first and noblest of all victories."

— Plato

LET'S IMAGINE A STACKABLE WOODEN RING TOY that is used to help babies improve their hand-eye coordination (see picture below). Now, imagine you have four rings, each representing a part of us (in no specific order): Mind, Physical, Religious/Spiritual, Psychological. The central stick represents our "being" or "self." This is what I will call *The Being Pyramid.* In this case, when the rings are aligned, the structure is most stable. So, if one could imagine aligning (or trying to align) their imaginary rings, the process alone would increase self-worth and self-esteem and build a more centered, stable, and happier individual. Now, if one of these rings is ignored, this pyramid would become misaligned and unstable. And although our being/self (central-stick) is still upright, the entities that make up the whole self are imbalanced.

I believe the misalignment of our rings plays a significant role in keeping one ill and perpetuating illness.

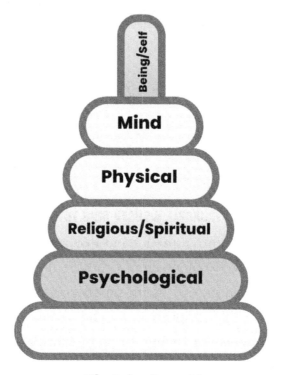

The Being Pyramid

In one study, published in 2018 in the *European Journal of Rheumatology*, there was a correlation between significant childhood trauma (known as ACE—adverse childhood events) and developing autoimmune (rheumatic) disease in adulthood. During 2018-2021, I worked as the Chief Physician in a Level 4 prison, where most inmates had significant childhood trauma from neglect, sexual, emotional and/or physical abuse. Interestingly, the amount of autoimmune disease prevalent within the prison walls is striking. The CDC corroborates this information clearly: *ACEs are linked to chronic health problems, mental illness, and substance misuse in adulthood.*[1]

Physicians are classically overworked and have precious little time during the day to tend to their inner space. I myself had a poor meditation practice until I discovered Eckhart Tolle, author of *The Power of Now* and *A New Earth*. He writes, "Just take four breaths a day to start." That's when I created the *Auscultation Meditation* (Auscultation is the Latin word for listening to parts of the body to aid in diagnosis).

Most general physicians (internists or family practice) see an average of 20 (or more) patients per day and listen to about 14 or so chests. I listen to each chest with my stethoscope in four areas, so the way I see it, that is 56 uninterrupted breaths (14 x 4=56) which I can use in a meditative way *while* seeing patients.

THE AUSCULTATION MEDITATION:

Put on your stethoscope and notice how silent it is. Notice how pronounced the sound of your breath becomes. Place one hand on their shoulder and the stethoscope on their back and close your eyes. "Really deep breath now," you say, as you tap on their shoulder gently. Magically, their breath becomes the predominant sound in your ears; at this point, your breaths synchronize. Tap their shoulder, indicating to take another breath and move to the next zone, and repeat the process. Pay the utmost attention to their breath. Notice as your hearing becomes highly acute. All that exists are the breaths you and your patient share. You are connected.

This process allows me to pick up subtleties in their lung sounds that may have eluded me otherwise. I do this for all four lung zones. I stand there for one second as I remove my stethoscope from my ears. I open my eyes, and for a short moment, the world is bright, still, silent, and calm. This is how I know my 'Auscultation Meditation' worked. "Sounds good!" I say (or whatever it sounded like). My patient doesn't even know what I have just done.

A Depressing Tale of Healthcare

"The trouble with the rat race is that even if you win, you're still a rat."

— Lily Tomlin

I ALWAYS DESPISED SUNDAYS BECAUSE it represented another week of misery approaching. This was a weekly feeling I had towards the end of my job at an HMO (Health Maintenance Organization). With my love for medicine and gratitude for having a job, I thought, how did it get to this point? What led me to feel so much sadness and frustration about healthcare? I used to have this naïve idea that medicine should be about patients. Boy was I wrong! After working in the mainstream corporate medical field for many years, I discovered that patient care made up only about 50% of my job. I had no idea that after 11 years of schooling and training, I would spend the other 50% of my time doing clerical work.

In late 2009 I started working for an organization that was primarily HMO-driven. It was well-established with a good reputation and competent staff. One year out of residency, I settled into this new job with enthusiasm and a romanticized vision of how I wanted to practice medicine. I was making a reasonable salary and on a path, to becoming a shareholder; I could support my family doing what I love. I thought, "What more could one ask for?" Quickly, my patient load was ramping up from 10 per day (training numbers) to 18-25 per day, and at times, 30 or more.

A family practice physician deals with many ailments from head to toe, and because we are the front line of medicine, patients usually see us first for most of their problems. In primary care, a patient rarely presents with one complaint; most people average about three of varying complexity. Unfortunately, handling everything in one visit is challenging, leaving the patient frustrated because they now must return for another appointment and pay another copay. It's a systemic problem that fails to put patients first. These organizations will tell you that "patients are the priority" and "double and triple booking is necessary for patients to be seen when they need it." In theory, this seems reasonable, but patients suffer and receive lower-quality care when physicians are over-booked.

As I matured as a man and a physician, I started to see the writing on the wall: There were not enough doctors to support the number of patients, and bureaucracy overwhelmed the process. The government insidiously revealed its presence by instituting pay-for-performance compensation. Patient care was becoming more about meeting bureaucratic goals and less about meeting our patients' goals. Staff was micromanaged, while doctors were scrambling to meet these quotas, leaving the remainder of the burden to the already overwhelmed support staff (without extra compensation). Letters were written to patients, telling them when specific tests were due and when to come in for a visit. The motivation here was less about patient care and more about meeting quotas. I was disheartened. I felt like an island. The reality of the system slowly doused the flame of my initial idealism.

Before long, a new "catch-phrase" came into fashion, PCMH (Patient-Centered Medical Home). As defined by the American College of Physicians, the Patient-Centered Medical Home is a care delivery model whereby patient treatment is coordinated through their primary care physician to ensure they receive the necessary care when and where they need it, in a manner they can understand. Thanks, and is this really a new concept? Corporate medicine loves to create redundancy by taking an existing concept and slapping a new name on it. They call this innovation. I call it lipstick on a pig. Its goal is *supposed* to increase patient satisfaction (we get bonuses for this) and improve patients' overall health-care experience by integrating a multi-disciplinary approach.

We had numerous meetings about this—I'm talking hours and hours of them—from learning how to pitch the new PCMH approach using all the skills of a used-car salesperson, to assigning mundane and arbitrary tasks to the support staff. Despite its robust implementation, PCMH was a failure. It was disorganized and made things convoluted and inefficient. While implemented in good faith, their efforts failed to make this one-size-fits-all approach to medicine successful. I started to feel like a hamster on a wheel seeing patient after patient. I continued to feel over-whelmed and discouraged. I needed more out of medicine, and I know my patients wanted more out of me.

I felt hopeless that things could be different until one patient casually asked me, "Dr. Mike, when are you going to open your concierge practice?" My jaw dropped. This patient unknowingly gifted me the inspiration to propel me to the next part of my career. I immediately called my wife and told her I knew what I wanted to do next. After seeing me unhappy for so long, she was excited about my newly found inspiration. From that moment on, I could see an end in sight. I stayed around for the next year and a half to let my pension vest, giving us some financial cushion after leaving. I called the bank on January 4, 2015, to secure a loan. By March 22, 2015, I had a small business loan (not so small) which would allow me to open my private practice.

While I am relieved to be out of the HMO, I sincerely appreciate the security and education they provided me during the early years of my career. However, it was unfair of me to stay, knowing I couldn't give them what they needed.

In the end, it was mutually beneficial.

PLEASE STAND AT AN ARM'S LENGTH FROM THE PERSON IN FRONT OF YOU

"Physicians are many in title but very few in reality."

— Hippocrates

I WAS SITTING IN A MEETING WITH MY coworkers at my corporate HMO job. Four of us were having a lunch meeting to bounce thoughts and ideas off one another on how to handle treatments of various medical concerns. Today's topic was depression.

One of my colleagues asked me, "Michael, how do you treat depression?" I responded, "Well, first, I talk to my patients and obtain a thorough history. I like to get to know them and find out the source of their so-called depression. I don't immediately jump on the diagnosis because people can have depressing thoughts, feelings of depression, and grief while not meeting a true diagnosis of depression." They chimed back, "So what do you do then?" "I talk to them," I said, shrugging. "Do you mean do I give them medicine?" They all nodded and said, "Yes." "Not always and not often. Like I said, most depression doesn't require medication." I continued, "It's our job to get to know our patients and stop taking away their growth opportunities by medicating it out of them." They looked at me with bewilderment. Cue the crickets. I thought I better end this, so I asked, "What do you do?" As I threw an upwards head nod to my co-worker to my left. He said, "Well, if someone has been depressed for two weeks, I give them medicine." "Huh?" I exclaimed reflexively. "Yes, according to the DSM-IV, if someone has been depressed for two weeks, they should be treated with medicine." I interjected, "I know that's what the DSM says, but do you really think that the right treatment? Hell, I've felt depressed for two weeks and it was fleeting." Once again, bewilderment followed by silence. I asked, "Are you worried about not treating someone and then they commit suicide?" "Yes." "So, you are treating to protect yourself from litigation?" "We have to," he said. I left frustrated but understood the predicament.

So, why are doctors not treating the patient and only the diagnosis? Is it the doctor's fear of litigation?

Time availability? Fear of being too personal or getting too close? Not sure how to ask the right questions? My best guess is probably a mix of all the above. For the moment, let's focus on professional distance. In medicine, maintaining professional distance is encouraged, yet we are expected to show empathy and compassion. It's an oxymoron at best. I believe if physicians identify too much with their role as a physician, it can get in the way of patient and professional interactions. Our white coat, though offering comfort to some patients due to its professional appearance and social status, may erroneously set up a power differential between us.

But let's be frank, a coat is a coat. It's a piece of cotton. It's when physicians find themselves so identified with their job that they *become* their job and robotic in their doctoring.

The *Rod of Asclepius,* an ancient symbol with one staff and one serpent, was originally named for the deity associated with healing and medicine. In modern medicine, however, the *Caduceus* is the universal medical symbol, with a staff and two serpents slithering from the bottom to the top. Many believe the two serpents represent the art and science of medicine. I think a crucial element is missing in the symbolism: our shared humanity.

Caduceus   *Rod of Asclepius*

The ability to authentically connect with patients is the key to understanding *them,* not just their disease. Patients are more than a number, diagnosis, or collection of symptoms. The aptitude for connecting on a deeper level to your patients, I believe, is *mostly* an innate quality. This ability makes it hard *not* to connect with the person/patient in front of you. I think classes on compassion and empathy are inherently futile, as our patients instinctively feel the insincerity.

Our past and over-identification with our own stories has a lot to do with how we interact on deeper levels in the present. One may keep distance for multiple reasons such as fear of loss, core beliefs about our worth or other life experiences that have *proven* that closeness yields pain—a foreshadowing that everything is transient. Some physicians have told me that emotional distance between them and their patients helps maintain a sense of objectivity. Yet, many physicians claim there is no time to connect because of the daily demands put upon them to see large volumes of patients. Which is it? I wonder, if providers had unlimited time, would that change the way they connect?

This commonly held belief may be worth re-evaluating. I don't think we necessarily lose objectivity when we allow for more meaningful connections with our patients. In my experience, closeness improves objectivity, like treating a family member. Even when grieving my patients, I never regretted letting them into my heart because I believe both of our lives were enriched by our connection.

What Do a Pub and an MRI Have in Common?

... They both make doctors feel better.

— Michael Lewis, MD

DURING 2003, I STUDIED IN LONDON at Kingston Hospital. I was never far from the hospital as I lived on campus in a repurposed nursing home dorm. I spent most days and nights in the hospital, seeing patients and learning the art of medicine, while also getting an education in government-run healthcare. The political climate around healthcare wasn't as heated as it is now, and classical healthcare reform wasn't on the radar for most people.

In the UK, the NHS (National Health Service) is the "free" government-run healthcare system—a misnomer at best, because NHS healthcare is subsidized by taxing the citizens at high rates. The training was quite different in the UK concerning schooling, board exams, and patient care. In London, I was taught that the physical exam is most critical. Scans (MRI and CT) should only validate what you think you found during a physical exam, which is the inverse of US standard of practice in urgent settings: scan first, then confirm with a physical exam. The training there is very patient-focused. We were taught to listen closely, obtain thorough histories and examine them using standard techniques.

I'm reminded of the time my father in-law was in the hospital and had a common side effect:

My father-in-law, Tom, was recently admitted into the Neuro-ICU at one of the best hospitals in California after sustaining a subarachnoid hemorrhage (brain bleed from a broken blood vessel—aneurysm). It was approximately day 8 of his stay, and he complained of lower abdominal pain all morning. He didn't have a fever, chills, or change in his bowel habits. The nurse said, "Don't worry, Tom, it's probably nothing. I'll tell the doctor." The nurse returns for a second time. "We are gonna get you an x-ray of your abdomen." Five hours passed, and no x-ray was done. The pain was becoming excruciating. The nurse comes in for the third time, "Let me check on that x-ray for you, Tom" It's now the eighth hour, and no x-ray. I called my dad, and I asked about his pain. "Michael, it's not any better and getting worse." "I'll be right over!" Jenn and I drove to the hospital, which was only 1.5 miles away from where we were staying. I arrived and saw dad was very uncomfortable. I sat at the foot of his bed, "Dad, where's your pain?" He points to the center of his lower abdomen, under his belly button. "Let me examine you." I walked over to him, gently put my hand on his belly, and knew the diagnosis instantly. "Are you fucking kidding me?" His bladder, which is normally not able to be felt, was sitting just beneath his belly button. I said, "Dad, your bladder is the size of a 20-week uterus (that's how I always measured the size of an enlarged bladder in men or women), which is big! Hold on." I walked to the large sliding door of his room and flagged down the nurse. She walked over to me presuming what I was about to say, "His x-ray is going to happen soon." "He doesn't need an x-ray," I said. She looked stumped. I continued, "He has acute urinary retention and needs a catheter. Please come here." The nurse comes into the room for the fourth time to see my dad. She stood beside him. I stood across from her. "Feel his bladder . . . gently," I directed. She felt his bladder. Surprised, her head moved back a few inches, her eyebrows raised, and she looked up at me. "That's why you touch your patient," I said firmly. "Please go get the doctor. He's been suffering for at least 8 hours."

Finally, the doctor arrived and said, "So, I hear you

think he has urinary retention." I thought, "What an
asshole." "Yes, his bladder is at the level of his umbilicus;
in fact, he probably has 1500 cc of urine retained," I
said confidently. She felt him, "Yes, he's retaining urine.
Let's get a catheter and a bladder ultrasound." They
return within 5 minutes. The ultrasound reads,
"750cc." I could tell the doctor was satisfied that I was
supposedly wrong with the volume. They inserted the
foley catheter, and his relief was instant. The final
urine volume collected was exactly 1500cc!
I tried to hide my smug satisfaction, unsuccessfully.
Dad fully recovered.

In the US, most people get scanned as soon as they
enter the emergency room. While this may seem benign
or even best practice, exploring the motivations behind
doing it this way is critical. In the US, the primary
motivation is quite simple: fear of litigation. The "CYA"
(cover your ass) mentality lives at the forefront of every
US practicing physician and usually dictates their
decision-making process. In the UK, the government sets
restrictions on MRIs, limiting the number of daily scans
a hospital can have. Doctors, therefore, must rely on
evidence-based medicine (EBM), *instinct*, patient
interaction, and physical exam skills.

I illustrate these differences not to compare which

healthcare system is better, but to highlight the model of student training in the US. It's important to realize how technology may interfere with establishing patient connections. Conversely, limiting scans may miss important life-saving information. Still, it's essential to acknowledge that technology and patient connections are not mutually exclusive. Perhaps shifting the focus to the patient will allow physicians to do a better job overall.

READY. SET. GO! DONE.

"The tighter you squeeze, the less you have."

— Thomas Merton

IN THE US, WE LIVE IN A FREE-MARKET SOCIETY where capitalism allows entrepreneurs to have a chance at fulfilling their dreams of owning their own business, free from government intrusion. I, like many others, like money. I also like organizations making money. However, I despise medical organizations persuading patients to join by falsely promising them better healthcare yet, delivering subpar care. I don't believe this is malicious, but it is the unintended consequence of an increasingly bureaucratic system where the focus is fat pockets, not healthier patients.

It's not only in the United States that a free market society, based on capitalism, exists. Though many believe that the government-driven, tax-subsidized NHS in the UK is the only option for them, my experience is a bit different:

It was my first rotation as a third-year medical student in Kingston Hospital, London. It was a Monday, and I was starting on the cardiology team. I've heard stories that if you want to watch procedures and assist, you must make yourself known and ask the attending. So, I arrived on the cardiology ward, and saw Dr. M, the cardiologist attending who would be my supervisor for the next few weeks. There were about 6 other members of the team including medical students, and other local young physicians. I saw Dr. M standing alone so I made my move and with one deep breath I said, "Dr. M? Hi, my name is Michael Lewis and I'm a medical student on your service for the next few weeks. I was wondering if I could tag around with you and observe procedures." He answered, "Absolutely! Meet me in front of the hospital at 7 a.m. on Wednesday. "Thank you, sir, I'll see you then." I walked away pridefully, like I just got a girl's phone number. Wednesday rolled around and I'm waiting at the front of the hospital for Dr. M. Then I heard it. I looked right and saw what appeared to be a rolling orgasm. It was a cherry red, 2003 Ferrari 360 Modena. He pulls up slowly as the video-game-sounding engine quiets to a low purr. Wait, is that the engine I'm seeing through the clear trunk? I'm not a car guy, but this was more than a car. I open the door delicately and entered with all the grace of a ballerina.

"Good morning. You ready?" Dr. M. stated. "Yeah man, let's go," I said, taken aback by this whole scenario. We took off like a bat out of hell and hit the freeway at top speeds of 120 mph. He gripped the wheel at ten and two, shook it like an excited kid and said, "I. Love. This. Car!" We both laughed. We arrived at the clinic where he was going to see patients and he told me, "None of these patients are NHS patients. They are all private pay." I thought, it all made sense to me now—the NHS doesn't pay their docs 'this' much. We got out of the car and headed inside to see patients for the day.

With British medicine being under relatively strict government control, certain things get delayed, especially cardiac catheterization and heart surgeries. For most minor things, the NHS handles medicine very well. But, when it comes to larger issues like cardiac catheterization, the motto is, *"don't die before we can see you in six weeks."* The astute Dr. M saw a gap in the market and made himself available for private pay diagnostic and therapeutic procedures. Instead of patients waiting six weeks for their cardiac procedure, Dr. M. could handle within the week for cash.

As evidenced by his car, he was a busy cardiologist.

"No Soup for You!"

— The Soup Nazi

HERE'S AN EXCITING EXPERIMENT. Ask any physician this simple question: Who is your employer? If they have a private practice, they will likely say, "no one" or "myself," or if they work for an organization, they will likely say the organization's name. The reality is (in a traditional model) they work for insurance companies. Why? When physicians fill out their patients' chart notes, they must specifically designate what are called E and M (evaluation and management) codes, which are essential for physicians or medical groups to get reimbursed (paid). The coding process is overly convoluted.

A typical office visit that gets reimbursed for $120, if not coded properly, can be significantly less, or denied. To make matters worse for the physician, the coding process is becoming more complicated every year.

All the while, insurance companies continue to circumcise reimbursements, causing physicians to add more patients to their already bloated schedules to make up for this cut. Over-booking leads to hurried visits, long wait times, diminished physician access, poor patient satisfaction, and an increased risk of missing diagnoses due to higher physician demands.

In no uncertain terms, insurance companies reduce patients into numbers (codes) and diagnoses. Sadly, physicians fall right in line behind them. I mean, what choice do we have?

Since doctors are at the mercy of insurance companies, they have no choice but to accept the rules entirely.

Without making you want to close the book out of sheer boredom, let's just say the ICD-10 (book of medical codes) got a well-needed overhaul in 2015. Unfortunately, the overhaul added significant complications for providers, some may say, making it easier for insurance companies to deny claims (a positive, unintended consequence for them). In one of my favorite *Seinfeld* episodes, "The Soup Nazi,"[2] the medical billing paradigm just mentioned is well illustrated:

Jerry finds a new soup shop that makes the best soup anyone has ever tasted. The only problem is that the owner, who's earned the nickname the Soup Nazi [insurance companies], is an angry eccentric. Despite warnings to the contrary [complicated billing], both George and Elaine fail to follow the 'rules' and suffer the consequences. Their order [insurance claim] was denied— "No soup for you!"

I ask again, who does the physician in the traditional model of medicine really work for?

THE LAST STRAW ...
OR IS IT?

"You will burn, and you will burn out; you will be healed and come back again."

— Fyodor Dostoevsky, *The Brothers Karamazov*

IT WAS A BUSIER DAY THAN USUAL. I was standing in my office, preparing to see my next patient. An endless stream of tasks flowed into my computer faster than I could take care of them. Tasks represent my clerical duties, such as returning patient calls and reviewing labs, x-rays, and hospital records. It wasn't unusual for my task list to hit over 100 every day. Adding insult to injury, I was the doctor of the day (DOD)—this may conjure images of balloons, banners, confetti, and congratulatory slaps on the back ... au contraire! The DOD's responsibilities include adding all the patient walk-ins into my already bloated schedule. Other "honored" tasks included re-ceiving all emergency phone calls while substituting for absent providers.

Unlike past days when I had these responsibilities, I felt oddly overwhelmed. A vagal sensation swept through me: My chest felt full. My throat felt tight. There was a pit in my gut as deep as the Grand Canyon, and my eyes filled with tears. I just stared at the door, paralyzed. Looking out my window to see the outside world, I felt like a prisoner longing for freedom. I contemplated running out of the building and never returning. I paced back and forth in a two-foot rectangle to soothe my mounting anxiety. "Hi Dr. Lewis, your patient is ready." "Thank you," I said. I shook it off and chalked it up to a fleeting moment of despair. But this wasn't the first time I had felt this way. Sometime later that night, I would think, "What am I doing there?" And "Is this really what I want for my career?" My work life was like *Groundhog Day*, a repetitive stream of endless tasks with no end in sight. I was at a crossroads in my life.

I asked myself, "How did I get here?" I suddenly realized that I was trading in my integrity for financial and career security. I was in danger of losing all I held dear. In his book *The Power of Now*, Eckhart Tolle says (paraphrased), if you don't like a situation, there are three things you can do:

1) Leave the situation.

2) Change the situation.

3) Accept the situation.

This idea held significant meaning and potential for me. I started by trying to let go of resistance and simply accepting the situation. I told myself, "It is what it is, and now it's time to let go of my idealistic view of medicine." I tried. That lasted a week or so. Next, I tried to change some things, so I rearranged my office to give it some new life, but that was like someone trying to convince themselves that they are not bald while sportin' a sweet comb-over. These options failed to provide peace and clarity, so my only option was to leave.

"Shit!"

It was a scary moment. I felt trapped. I couldn't stay, and I couldn't leave. I had a family to take care of and over $300,000 in student loans to repay.

In medical school, cautionary tales about burnout run rampant. I never thought this applied to me because I thought this only happens to emergency room doctors. Burnout is real. According to a retrospective study done in 2016 by the American Medical Association, "Medical specialties with the highest burnout rates," Family Medicine had the third highest rate of physician burnout, while Emergency Medicine and Urology took up the top two spots, respectively. I was unprepared for this reality.

I was 39 years old, had only been with this company for five years, and I was laying like a wet match with little to no hope of igniting my fire, and I knew a radical change needed to happen . . . fast.

PART
TWO

THE WHITE COAT MENTALITY

26 INCHES OF INSECURITY

"Doctors will have more lives to answer for in the next world than even we generals."

— Napoleon Bonaparte

IT'S THE NIGHT BEFORE THE FIRST DAY OF MEDICAL SCHOOL, and all the new students are excited, as we are about to participate in The White Coat Ceremony. The idea originated at the University of Chicago's Pritzker School of Medicine in 1989, but the first full-fledged ceremony was at the Columbia University College of Physicians and Surgeons in 1993. The donning of the white coat has become a rite of passage for most incoming medical students. This ceremony marks the beginning of a long and challenging journey. The jacket is about 26 inches long, aptly called "The short white coat." It immediately distinguishes students amongst the "long coats," the real doctors. After the ceremony, they would hang unworn in our closets until our third year of school during our clinical rotations in the hospital.

• 43 •

Kingston Hospital, London, UK, Medical School, Third Year Clinical Rotations, Day 1:

I walk proudly down the hospital hallway with purpose and anticipation of what's to come. My coat pockets are overflowing: *The Pocket-Sized Oxford Handbook of Medicine, A Pocket Guide to Physical Examination and History Taking,* a ruler, an ophthalmoscope, an otoscope, a small book to write notes, and about 10 pens. As I strut down the hallways, I see them. The knowing eyes of the nurses and staff peering at me with a sympathetic head nod: "So, cute, aww, look at him, a little medical student." I shrugged it off and kept walking, though my inside thought was more like, "Suck it!"

Third-year medical students do what is commonly referred to as *scut work*—menial, tedious jobs from taking vital signs, scribing the notes and chasing down results from the lab, while some are not so glamorous:

I was in a group with six other medical students. On this day, we were discussing MRIs. The attending looked at me and said "You." I prepared myself to answer his questions. I was ready. Let's go. He nodded and said, "I'll take my tea white, thanks." I nodded back and said, "Sure thing, asshole." No, not really, but I wanted to. He received his hot, white tea promptly because even doing that right was a win for a third-year medical student.

Typically, we would arrive in the early morning to meet our team, made up of other medical students, house officers/senior house officers (like medical residents in the US), and the registrar (senior doctor) and attending physician. We would make our daily patient rounds and then gather in a semicircle for the daily "pimp session." Getting pimped in medicine is where the attending asks questions about the patient's illness, cause, and other esoteric information. For example: What's the third most common cause of X? Or the least effective treatment of Y? What labs will you draw to check to see if X is causing Y? Etc. Some attendings send you to the library and kick you off the team for the rest of the day if you can't answer the questions correctly. While some can be belittling, others are encouraging. My best friend, Brent, and I were usually well-prepared. We had just finished our first of three board exams, the USMLE (United States Medical Licensing Examination) Step I, regarded as one of the most difficult tests written.[3] Before starting clinical rotations, this exam is required, covering extensive aspects of diseases down to the DNA level. On the wards, we shined. We would answer all the questions quickly and accurately, sometimes quicker and more detailed than our seniors—this was a function of the training difference (not necessarily the intelligence) between doctors in the US versus the UK. Other times, I got wicked tongue lashings, which would send me sulking back to my nursing home dorm room in tears. I would tell myself, "I know I'm a student, but I'm not supposed to know everything, right? Isn't that the definition of a student?" While I felt pride for having come this far, these moments would take a toll on my confidence as a student.

Still, we were "scut-monkeys" at the beck and call of our seniors. Though well-aware of the wisdom and purpose behind this dynamic, the active military-inspired crushing of one's confidence left me with only one central teaching point:

It taught me what kind of doctor/teacher I didn't want to be.

40 Inches of Ego

"How starved you must have been that my heart became a meal for your ego."

— Amanda Torroni

DURING MY THIRD YEAR AS A MEDICAL STUDENT, I was the first assistant on a hemicolectomy (a surgery done to remove part of the colon—in this case, for severe diverticulitis). I was staring into the open abdomen of a woman while holding back the abdominal tissue with a large stainless-steel retractor in both hands. My senior attending was dissecting her colon away from the surrounding tissues. The patient was draped in blue sterile dressings from her neck to her feet with a central opening, from the sternum (breastbone) to umbilicus (belly button). She was splayed open.

I had an excellent reputation as a medical student in the hospital and was often asked to join other teams. I ended up on a general surgery team during a one-month stint of a six-month surgical rotation. The registrar was the lead on the surgery. She stood directly across from me over the patient's abdomen. Her dislike of me was apparent, though I couldn't figure out why. Up until this point, she had been curt in our interactions. We didn't have much conversation prior, but it was always benign when we did. While we were operating, I was trying to anticipate her next move (seemingly, this is what makes a good assistant). She was silent all surgery and didn't teach at all. She didn't answer most questions, and if she did, it was usually with a short answer.

As she was closing the patient, I verbalized my understanding with a mumbled, "Uh-huh. Hmm-hmm." She peered harshly over her surgical mask at me as if she was trying to silence my vocal cords with her eyes. Muffled through her mask, she gritted harshly, "Can you just shut up!" I was embarrassed and shocked all at the same time. I was aware of everyone in the operating theater at that moment. I felt my heart drop because I would hate to make a wrong impression as a medical student, especially a third year. I wanted to believe her outburst was less about her dislike for me than what was happening inside of her. We ended the surgery, doffed our gowns and gloves, and didn't say a word to each other. She put on her 40" full-length doctor's coat and left the operating theater.

A few minutes passed, and we gathered with the other students and house officers to plan the next part of the day. As if I was invisible, she started berating me in front of everyone, "You wouldn't believe how loud and obnoxious Michael was." I was appalled. She continued, "He wouldn't shut up during the surgery, made noises, and just wouldn't stop." At this point, like any human with a pulse, my blood started to boil. As she was verbally vomiting her displeasure all over the team, I thought, "Hell no! What kind of devil is this?" I felt angry and waited for a break in her beratement. I took a small step toward her and said, "I'm sorry if I annoyed you. But I don't know who you think you are!" I responded forcefully and directly. "I am a human being, and I DO NOT deserve to be spoken to like that . . . ever!" The other residents and students who surrounded us gasped and looked down in horror. Apparently only "full-fledged" doctors are supposed to have backbones. I stood and looked her dead in the eyes for what seemed like an eternity. At this moment, we crossed into *Kairos* (the moment where the felt sense of chronological time stops existing). The silence was deafening. I turned around and walked away. Quickly, word spread through the hospital of what had happened, and many supported me. I was never spoken to like that again in the hospital for the remainder of my third year. She never apologized.

For some, it seems that once they are gifted the *long white coat*, they forget what it was like to be the student.

Aww, Nuts!

*"I don't look in the mirror and think that I have flaws.
I actually look in the mirror and see me. I see a lot of
different characters and a lot of different things."*

– Elisha Cuthbert

PHYSICIANS TEND TO FORGET that they are patients too. When I see patients, I remember that they could very well be me or a family member. When we lose touch with that idea, I believe our patients' treatment won't be the best that we can offer. Yes, someone can still perform heart surgery or another life-saving procedure expertly and save a life, but to dismiss the emotional component of our patients is doing a disservice.

Being overly identified in our roles (in any job), can create a power differential that may inhibit connections with others. So, why does it occur? Ego, fear, self-preservation, maintaining professional distance, and in-ability can all be obstacles. Part of the reason for writing this book is to invite reflection and offer tools to open more possibilities.

Physician expertise is important, but one would hope they went into medicine for reasons other than their ability to pass tests.

I believe compassion is a reflection of our inner-self, expressed outwardly, and the lack of it may harm our patients, both physically and emotionally:

I was on the table anxiously awaiting the beginning of my vasectomy. I knew the surgeon well, having worked with him for many years. I was his patient now and trusted him implicitly for this surgery. This outpatient surgery typically lasts 30-60 minutes using local anesthesia (yes, a needle to the nuts). The surgeon was ready to start, so I was taken to the procedure table, prepped (cleaned with iodine), and draped while awaiting the start. He began by injecting a small amount of local anesthesia into my scrotum, midline, so he could make one small opening for access to the vas deferens. I should mention that I've performed a few of these surgeries using a relatively painless, no-scalpel technique, which limits pulling, pain, and recovery. He wasn't doing it this way. I thought, "Oh shit!"

Before I continue, I should mention some basic but not exhaustive anatomy. The spermatic cord contains many small structures. For simplicity, I will only discuss the genitofemoral nerve and the vas deferens. The vas deferens is a tube-like structure that carries sperm away from the testicles to the urethra. During a vasectomy, it's split, preventing sperm from traveling through the penis. The genitofemoral nerve is one that every man protects with his life because when it gets activated by a kick or a strong wind, it hurts like the dickens (no pun intended). I digress.

He then used a small grasping instrument to grab my left spermatic cord. Silently, I screamed, "What the fuck is that?!" I felt like a bull with very large hoofs kicked me in the balls. My toes curled up until my feet went into spasm. He said casually, "The pain will disappear in a moment." The worst pain of my life diminished after 60 long seconds. Before I knew it, the left side was done. Yes . . . only the left. He had to do it again on the right. With a muffled voice, he said through his mask, "We're going to start the other side now." The cremasteric reflex became fully engaged—this reflex causes your testicles to shrink upwards into your abdomen from cold or fear. It was as if my testicular military troops just put on their muskets, helmets, and boots, packed their bags, raised their white flags, and screamed, "Retreat! Retreat!" The surgeon calmly said,

"You might feel a little pull again, but first, I need you to relax your testicles." A silent rage filled my mind, "What?! Relax my testicles?" I thought, "It's non-sensical. Apparently, this guy's nuts haven't been to war!" Yet, the bull kicked again, though it felt even harder this time. I thought, "Are you fucking kidding me? Did the hoofs get bigger?" "Jesus Christ, Doc!" I exclaimed. "Why don't you do the no-scalpel technique or at least a double incision to limit the pulling?" He said in a monotone voice, "Sometimes the vas swells when I numb it and occasionally makes it difficult for me to grab it using that technique, you know what I mean?" Now I was really pissed off because he wanted me to corroborate with him. I thought, "You had a choice and chose this way?"

He completed. They wrapped my testicles up like delicate little Christmas ornaments and discharged me. My wife was waiting for me and helped me get to the car. I slowly sat down in the passenger side and screamed, "That was a fucking nightmare!" Tears poured down my face. "That was the most painful thing I've ever had done!" I couldn't stop feeling it. Every time I closed my eyes, I relived it again and again and again.

The surgeon had another option that would've caused less mental and physical pain. Instead, he chose to do it in a way that was quicker to benefit *him*, not me, I presume. As a physician, my goal is to help people through their suffering and, at best, alleviate it altogether. I suffered on that table. I was in tears when I got back in the car with my wife because I knew there was an easier way that would've been more comfortable, and he didn't even take that into consideration, or did he?

The lack of connectedness isn't all about words; it's also in the silent exchanges during procedures. If he were here now, I would ask him: "If you were having a vasectomy and had a choice of how you would want it done, would you choose the most painful or least painful way?" If he said, "Midline incision," (like mine) I would call "bullshit!"

My toes still curl when I think about it.

A BRITISH TERMINATION

"Now, if you'll excuse me, I'm going to go home and have a heart attack."

— Vincent, *Pulp Fiction*

ALL I WANTED WAS TO WITNESS THIS procedure, and now I can't unsee it.

I was a third-year student at St. Peter's hospital in Chertsey, Surrey, UK doing my OB-GYN rotation. As medical students, we are encouraged to see and do as much as possible during this 4-week rotation. I performed Caesarian sections, hysteroscopies, and other surgical procedures. I heard it would be a good idea to go to the Early Pregnancy Unit (EPU) and watch the termination procedures (abortions). The following day, I arranged to meet with the gynecologist performing the procedure.

Warning, graphic imagery of an abortion procedure:

I arrived in the early afternoon to attend this session. There were two women on the schedule for today's abortions. Honestly, I wasn't prepared for what was about to happen. I wasn't scrubbed up or in fancy surgical gear. I was just wearing a gown. I walked into the dark room and saw Ms. W, a thirty-something woman lying on a chair under a spotlight, tilted back in stirrups. She was blonde, with strands of hair flowing from under her surgical cap. Her early, second-trimester baby had died in utero and had to be removed. At her feet was a large machine. It was cylindrical and came up to her ankles. It had a large tube attached to it. The obstetrician verified that the baby wasn't viable with an ultrasound and then rolled the ultrasound out of the way.

"Let's begin," the surgeon said.

The patient nodded. Wait, I thought, she's not going to be medicated? No sedation? The surgeon sat down at her open pelvis and pulled out a needle and syringe to anesthetize the cervix. This was all the anesthesia she would receive. He inserted the stainless dilators, gradually increasing in size to widen the cervical os (opening into the uterus). There must be enough room to insert the vacuum tube. There wasn't much talking. He grabbed the tube and slid it into her uterus. I looked down at Ms. W to see how she was doing. The surgeon finally spoke:

"Turn it on."

The vacuum whirred as it started sucking in the uterine contents. Ms. W's face was wincing. The not-so-subtle sound of a vacuum doing its job was disturbing, to say the least. The thud of the Products of conception (POC) forcefully exited the tube into the container. It wasn't like I was the only one hearing this, yet everyone remained quiet and still. Ms. W is lying there, eyes closed tightly as her crow's feet became intermittently pronounced. A tear rolled down to her temple. Thud. Another one. I thought, was it a body part? The fetal skull? A foot? How can you not think it was a body part, even if you knew it wasn't? This was a fucking horror film. Ms. W looks like she isn't in any physical pain. Thud. Another one? Finally, the chaotic sound of the vacuum became smooth as the last POC was removed.

There was nothing left.

The procedure completed, and I told Ms. W, I was very sorry as I put my hand on her left shoulder. I left the room. I didn't return for the second woman.

To my OB-GYN colleagues (US, UK, or anywhere in the world), I beg you to sedate your patients during a termination procedure. One could imagine it's hard enough deciding to terminate no matter the reason, but no patient should be conscious during that procedure and subjected to that kind of trauma.

That was one of the most gruesome moments of my career and the last termination procedure I ever attended.

Do as I Say ... or Don't

"As an actor there's no autonomy, unless you're prepared to risk the possibility of starving."

— Ben Kingsley

NOT ALL DECISIONS ARE OURS TO MAKE. Physicians are not the bosses of our patients, nor should we try to be. Medicine has evolved over the last hundred years from a paternalistic-based system to an autonomy-based (patient-centered) system. A patient-centered approach has finally put a lot of power back into the hands of the patient. However, with the advent of the internet, strong opinions garnered through their own research can create difficulties. Dr. Google has become many people's primary care physician. I find it most important in this profession to exercise a choice-outcomes model. In this way when patients are presented with the physician's data, expertise, experience, and evidence-based medicine they are better prepared to make informed decisions.

All outcomes are not the same; some may lead to harm, while others lead to improvement in symptoms or a cure. We see this most recently with CAM (complementary and alternative medicine). I support many complementary approaches and their role in patient care. Recently, more patients have become disenchanted with Western medicine and are finding alternative treatments for their ailments. Some work well, while others are erroneously presented as "cures" to patients. To make an informed and educated decision, patients should be given all information necessary before beginning a standard treatment or an alternative one (informed consent).

In some cases, mainly cancer, some patients have chosen to use alternative therapies such as herbs and other non-medical methods, which haven't shown much, if any, statistical benefit, except what's being propagandized on the internet. Alternative therapies can sometimes be reasonable, especially if they're *complementary*, not *exclusionary* of medical therapy. If medical therapy is delayed too long, the therapeutic window may pass, leaving the patient feeling impotent and hopeless.

Some of the most difficult conversations doctors will encounter are discussions about end-of-life situations and when to withdraw life support. These decisions are never easy for the doctor or the decision-maker and carries with it great responsibility. The best thing I can do is help this person understand that they are making the right decision based on all data we know, which I can only hope will assuage guilt or regret:

Mr. Craig was an 84-year-old male in cardio-respiratory failure on a ventilator. I was the senior resident in charge of the CCU (coronary care unit) at Fairview Hospital in Cleveland, Ohio. Mr. Craig had been at the hospital for about two and a half weeks. He was a full code (per his wishes, if his heart or breathing stopped, we would do everything in our power to save his life). Sadly, it got to a point where it was determined that Mr. Craig couldn't survive off the ventilator; therefore, his wife would have to be burdened with making a tough decision to discontinue the ventilator and say goodbye forever. She would come in daily and sit with him for hours. Because I was Mr. Craig's physician in this unit, I was responsible for letting Mrs. Craig know that it didn't look like he was going to improve and that she would have to decide to withdraw life support soon. It's crucial to be very straightforward, as false hope is cruel. I would sincerely ask, "Mrs. Craig, I know this isn't easy, but what do you want to do?" "I don't know," she would say. "Okay, let me know if you have any questions," I consistently responded. This night was probably the most challenging day I had ever had as a medical student or resident, and in retrospect, as a doctor.

A different patient, Mrs. Patel in Room 5, has gone into cardiac arrest for the fourth time in two hours. I was running the code, which means I was directing the doctors and nurses on what to do, where to do it, what medications to give to the patient, analyze the EKG, and decide how long we continue the code.

Unfortunately, Mrs. Patel died shortly after her fourth time coding. I had to pronounce her.

Later that night, Mrs. Kirby—a married mother of three—came up to our floor in respiratory failure. I looked at her chest x-ray before she came up. I bowed my head in futility. I knew she was going to die soon, if not tonight. I met the family and got her settled in when she came up. I consulted with the attending, and we decided that she should receive all the pain meds that were ethically feasible. She died the next morning. The same evening, Mrs. Craig, the wife of the gentleman on the ventilator, came in. She said, "I'm ready." I said, somewhat surprised, "Are you sure?" She looked down and said, "Yes."

I walked with her into her husband's room, where he lay still, breathing with the use of the ventilator only. She sat on the edge of his bed. She held his wrinkled left hand, and suddenly I had a vision of the first time they did this. "This is as real as it gets," I thought. "Are you ready?" I asked. "Okay, doctor," she said with trepidation. I turned off the ventilator and kept the vital sign monitor on. The silence was deafening as the shushing sound of the ventilator ceased to pump life into Mr. Craig. I stayed in the room out of the way. She caressed his hands and said, "Thank you for being such a good loving man to me all these years. You can go now, honey. It's okay. I'll see you soon. I love you. It's okay, honey. You can go now." Tears were welling up in my eyes as I saw the end of this beautiful couple and the grief that was to come. His heart rate was slowing: 45, 36, 24, 20, 15 . . . asystole (flatline). There was no long beep, like in the movies, because I silenced the monitor. It was his final countdown that began with his first beat after conception.

I gave my loving condolences with a hug and a kiss on Mrs. Craig's cheek. She stayed with him. I walked over to Mr. Craig, put my hand on his head, kissed his forehead, and whispered, "Rest in peace, Mr. Craig." My wife, Jen, showed up to bring me dinner almost as soon as I finished in the room with Mr. and Mrs. Craig. We went to a private, quiet room to eat.

I broke down crying—what a night.

It's been almost 20 years since that night in the CCU, and it still brings me to tears. I didn't need a wall to protect myself from the emotions that I was feeling or to maintain professional objectivity. My grief solidified the view that such closeness doesn't interfere with objectivity. If allowing deeper connections to my patients or their loved ones during the final moments of life can make death just a little easier, then why not? Everyone benefits. Sitting with people as they take their last breaths helps me reflect on my relationship with death. It helps me find the courage to face it and try to harness the power to improve my life, despite its inevitable outcome. Death is our most challenging teacher, but its lessons are vital.

THE OLD WAYS...
THE NEW WAYS

"You don't have to be a genius; you just have to have passion and a burning desire to move forward."

— Moya Mulvay

IT MUST'VE BEEN MY FIRST WEEK IN the A&E (accident and emergency, the UK's emergency room), and I was walking behind my attending physician, as I heard him say, "Let's make her a DNR." Umm. I thought, wait, the doctors make that decision, not that patient? Where am I?

Patient-centered or autonomy-based medicine has evolved slowly over time and is now widely accepted; conversely, a paternalistic approach has become politically unpopular.[4] In 2001, The Institute of Medicine (IOM) defined patient-centered care as "providing care that is respectful of and responsive to individual patient preferences, needs, and values and ensuring that patient values guide all clinical decisions." In certain public health situations, we must consider what is best for society even if patients are unhappy with the recommendation or directive, such as isolation or quarantine due to illnesses like Covid-19, active tuberculosis, or other health crises.

"Autonomy" comes from the Greek *autos* (self) and *nomos* (rule, governance, or law) and was first used to refer to self-government or self-rule. Beauchamp and Childress[5] describe it as the "personal rule of the self that is free from both controlling interferences by others and personal limitations that prevent meaningful choice, such as inadequate understanding." In a medical context, respect for a patient's autonomy is considered a fundamental ethical principle and is the central premise of *informed consent:* a process of communication between you and your healthcare provider that often leads to agreement or permission for care, treatment, or services. Informed consent needs to consider extrinsic factors (force, coercion, or manipulation) and intrinsic factors (level of consciousness and cognitive level) so that a patient can make a well-informed decision. One example of *managing* an intrinsic factor would be controlling cancer pain so that it doesn't cloud the patient's judgment—for instance, "I would rather die than feel this type of pain."

Charles, Whelan, et al.[6] developed a framework for analyzing treatment-related decision-making. They define three categories: *The paternalistic,* characterized by physician control. *The informed approach,* defined by a division of labor between physician and patient (autonomy), and *the shared approach,* where both the physician and patient have equal input. Whereby most patients in the US want to be completely informed of their medical situation, a large cross-sectional survey conducted among the American public using computer-assisted telephone interviewing found diverse responses regarding the preferred approach. The results found that 62% of respondents preferred shared decision-making, 28% preferred the informed approach and 9%preferred paternalism.[7] [8]

To add to the complexity of a pure autonomous medical relationship, about 20% of patients would rather not know the full extent of their medical condition. In comparison, about 10% prefer to leave the decisions to their family or physician.[9]

As we saw in Mr. Craig's scenario, the legal aspect of the family making decisions for their loved one was seemingly straightforward because Mr. Craig had named his wife the medical power of attorney (MPOA). The MPOA is a legal process of designating someone as the sole medical decision-maker for the individual.

However, not all decisions require an MPOA, as the hospital (ethics committee if needed) will defer to either the spouse or next of kin if no MPOA was selected. Section 313.004 of the Health and Safety Code states that if an adult patient in a hospital is incapacitated, an adult can act as a surrogate.[10] In the order of priority, the following people can consent to treatment:

- Your spouse.
- Your adult child, with the waiver and consent of all other qualified adult children.
- The majority of your children.
- Your parents.
- An individual clearly identified to act on your behalf before you became incapacitated.
- Your nearest living relative or a member of the clergy.

This process becomes more complex when there *isn't* an MPOA. When siblings who haven't participated in the direct care of their family member feel they should have the same input as the family member who has been the sole care provider, the situation can be heated:

Mrs. Patel (the patient that went into cardiac arrest

four times earlier) was a 79-year-old female recently brought up from the medical floor into the CCU for respiratory failure. She had multiple medical problems, was frail due to her age, had congestive heart failure, and had a history of breast cancer. Joe, her son, was the primary caregiver and sitting by her side. She was a full code (wanted all life-saving measures). He wasn't his mom's medical power of attorney but had been his mom's sole caregiver for two years. He knew the ins and outs of her daily routine, her decubitus ulcers, her doctor's appointments, and her current state of health better than anyone else. Joe had two siblings: a brother that lived an hour away and a sister that lived out of state. The brother who lived close by understood that Joe is responsible for his mom's care and trusted his decision-making abilities, while the sister who lived out of state (and just arrived in the CCU), didn't know what was happening.

I gathered the three of them around the counter at the nurses' station to discuss life-saving decisions for their mother. The sister wanted us to do everything, while Joe thought it would be best to let her go peacefully and not perform CPR or give her any other life-saving measures. As we were talking, a siren rang through the hospital, "Code blue CCU Room five, code blue CCU Room five, code blue CCU Room five." I turned around, and Mrs. Patel was in cardiac arrest. I told the family, "I must try resuscitating your mom." I turned around and hurried to her room which was 15 feet away. The telemetry monitor showed asystole (flatline). I directed the nurse to start compressions on her chest. "Ribs broke," the nurse said as she continued compressions. She was on a ventilator already. I called for one milligram of epinephrine. Compressions went on for a couple of minutes, before I called out, "Hold the compressions." Her heart rate resumed, and I stood next to the monitor for a couple of minutes to ensure the patient's stability. "Stay here," I told the nurse. I went out to talk to the family and told them she was alive now, but we needed to decide what to do should this happen again. It was a split. Joe and his brother wanted the DNR-CC, while his sister wanted all life-saving measures. Not five minutes passed when the overhead alarm went off again, "Code blue CCU Room five..."

I went back to the room, and this time a swarm of other doctors responded to the code as well. I called again to start CPR and give medicine. I called to hold compressions so we could read the heart monitor. She was in ventricular fibrillation (complete electrical disassociation of the heart—chaos). I called for the defibrillator, "Two-hundred joules, please." Another doctor took the paddles, placed them on her chest,

"Clear!" A small click from the defibrillator sent electricity to her heart—a control-alt-delete to the heart's CPU. Her legs and arms twitched slightly with the shock (unlike in the movies). "Still in V-fib," I said as I checked the monitor. "Charge to three-hundred." The defibrillator was charged, "Clear!" She was shocked again. I called to hold CPR to watch the monitor. She had a rhythm on the monitor, but no pulses felt. I thought, "PEA" (pulseless electrical activity). "Continue CPR," I said as I called for another milligram of epinephrine. We stopped after a couple of minutes to check the monitor, and this time she had a palpable pulse and a rhythm on the monitor; she was stable for the moment. We kept a nurse at the bedside to monitor.

I came back to update the family, and there was still discord between them. Mrs. Patel arrested two more times while the family deliberated on what to do. After the final attempt and 30 minutes of resuscitation, we couldn't revive her. I came out to the family to tell them the sad news. The family was grateful for the efforts. They knew we did all we could. They walked into her room for the last time and gathered around their mom. I pronounced her dead, and with my hand on her arm, and a kiss on her forehead, I whispered, "Rest in peace, Mrs. Patel." I left the room.

The sound of the drape closing defined the end of Mrs. Patel's final act

The family's delay in a clear decision led me to do everything to help Mrs. Patel, even if some of the family didn't want those extended efforts. The same is true when physicians believe rescue efforts would be futile and there isn't a DNR-CC in place. Knowing that life-saving measures would be ineffective, anything other than a brutally honest conversation with the family would be cruel. Recovery after the trauma of CPR would be difficult due to the patient's frailty, even if they did survive resuscitative efforts—CPR is violent and not for the faint of heart. In no uncertain terms, this must be clearly conveyed to the family. As physicians, we are programmed to prolong life and not give up until all efforts have been proven futile. When this situation presents itself, I believe quality (joy) of life should be considered over quantity (years), hands down.

CAN PATIENTS MAKE CHOICES FOR THEMSELVES?

"A lack of transparency results in distrust and a deep sense of insecurity."

— Dalai Lama

AS A RESIDENT IN FAMILY MEDICINE, I didn't learn to fully appreciate patient autonomy until the second year of my training, which really meant that I didn't trust my patients to care for themselves without me. This led to a very stressful patient-care experience. I felt I had to deal with every concern and ailment my patients had during their visit because if I didn't, and something happened to them, I felt it would be my fault. I took on more responsibility than needed, mainly because I was inexperienced and didn't know any better. I hadn't learned that patients are autonomous and can make decisions for themselves. I worried, after I sent them home, whether they would have the sense to call 911, go to the hospital, or call me. Being an overly concerned new doctor trying not to miss anything, made my work more stressful than it needed to be. I felt I bore all responsibility. Once I learned how to put the responsibility back on my patients, my stress levels decreased, my confidence increased, and my patient care improved tremendously.

Sometimes our patients make poor choices. That's just the way it is. Commonly, people want to leave the hospital for multiple reasons despite a physician's recommendations to stay: Before their infection is cured, leaving too soon after surgery, or not wanting to be admitted to the hospital when they have significant chest pain requiring evaluation. When this occurs, assuming the patient has proper decision-making capacity, they must sign a legal document releasing the medical staff of responsibility, an AMA (against medical advice)—full autonomy on the grandest scale. As long as the physician ensures the patient knows the risks and their chance of readmission or possibility of death (depending on the scenario), we don't have much say in patients leaving AMA. Interestingly, there are some exceptions to this rule of law, as federal officials have broad rights through the Centers for Disease Control (CDC).[11] For example, suppose an acutely ill patient with an infectious disease like active tuberculosis (which poses a considerable threat to the community) denies treatment and wants to sign out AMA from the emergency room. In that case, they can be arrested and held against their will *despite* autonomy and an AMA.

To summarize, patients have the right to deny, discontinue or delay medical therapy at any time if they are of legal age, cognitively intact, conscious, and aware of all the risks of doing so, if they don't pose a threat to the community.

We're on the Same Team, Aren't We?

"I want people in my life that are more interested in my growth than in my comfort."

— Eric Johnson

A PHYSICIAN'S OBJECTIVITY IS SOMETIMES TRICKY as we are not without our own judgments or biases. If physicians have a family of origin with less than stellar upbringing, insecurities, political leanings, or their own "baggage," it can be challenging to maintain objectivity. These issues, unexamined, can affect decision-making and our interactions.

Self-awareness is critical in facilitating the successful autonomous relationships that we are trying to create with our patients.

An important thing to remember in patient relationships is to accept where they are in their level of readiness to change. This is a crucial element practiced by psychotherapists and psychologists (hopefully psychiatrists) to set the foundation for a trusting relationship with their patients.

Most therapists meet their clients *where they are* in their current situation and help them confront obstacles to their healing. Therapists aren't there to give advice, tell clients where to go, what to do, and what actions to take; instead, they help them discover their motivations and find the courage to help *themselves* grow. Similar ideology should be present within the physician's office. I'm not advocating that we take the role of a therapist, but we should assess our patient's motivation for change and healthcare goals while not impeding the process with our own biases, even if we know their choices may cause them harm. Our job is to spell out the risks and benefits and let them decide. Even topics seemingly as benign as starting a blood pressure medicine must be a team effort.

The task sounds simple enough: "Your blood pressure has been high on multiple visits, and I think it's time we start a medicine for you." Patients may have contradictory feelings about this, which could be based on family members' or friends' past side effects from similar pills, people they know who have died while taking this pill, "Dr. Google" reporting (erroneously) that it would cause cancer, or perhaps what it *means to them* to take it in the first place. Meaning-making is a doorway into understanding our patients' inner-obstacles and is essential for improving compliance.

Whether recommendations come from "Dr. Google" or from our patients, it's important to validate their concerns, let them know they are heard, give them objective data, and provide comfort.

This increases the trust necessary for the kind of motivational interviewing required to help an ambivalent patient. When we fail to do this, we risk losing them (sometimes that's a blessing) and leave them vulnerable to harm.

Sometimes no amount of rapport or trust can impact an especially stubborn patient. But it's our duty to make the effort. This is where we practice *letting go* and accepting that our patients are ultimately responsible for their own well-being.

PART THREE

BALANCING MEDICINE
AND EXPERIENCE

LET'S PLAY SOME JAZZ!

"Some people are so narrow-minded that they can see through a keyhole with both eyes."

— Unknown

TO BE HONEST, I HAD NEVER READ the original definition of evidence-based medicine (EBM) until I wrote this section. Ironically, I used the ideas passed down from others to define it. The initial discussion of EBM was published in the *Journal of the American Medical Association* in 1992[12] and further honed, in the *British Medical Journal* in 1996. David Sackett, one of the founders of EBM, defines: "The practice of evidence-based medicine means integrating individual clinical expertise with the best available external evidence from systematic research."[13] Good doctors must use both individual clinical expertise and the best available external data to arrive at positive clinical outcomes because neither alone is enough. Without clinical experience, wisdom, and gut feeling, medical decisions leaning solely on EBM risk being pared down to robotic algorithms, which may not be enough or even appropriate. Conversely, out-of-date treatments could harm the patient or delay a cure in the absence of utilizing the most current research.

We all can agree that EBM is important and a necessity; where it becomes problematic is when physicians use EBM like following recipes in a cookbook. Like most things in this world, there needs to be a fulcrum (balance) between two ideas to arrive at the best solution. In this case, healing is the fulcrum that experience and EBM teeter upon:

Balancing these two entities takes us out of the checklist-oriented visit and allows for freedom to think out of the box. Conversely, when clinical experience is their only approach doctors can fall into the trap of doing the same old things they've been doing for years. Without keeping up with the literature to learn new and better ways to care for their patients, there can be negative consequences. A case in point:

Mrs. H was a 47-year-old female with Rheumatoid Arthritis (RA). She was diagnosed elsewhere but came to see me for alternative therapies. She didn't want to be on the classic medications for RA, DMARDs (disease-modifying anti-rheumatic drugs), which tend to be hard on the body and can carry severe side effect profiles. We ran some blood tests to verify her disease process, checked multiple markers for RA, and checked the extent of inflammation. We validated her RA. I was ready to go with the evidence, but she was willing to try alternative means to help her pain. We discussed high-dose Omega-3 fatty acids (anti-inflammatory) and a cox-2 inhibitor once daily (an anti-inflammatory with little effects on the stomach). She had some relief but wanted to try something else. She brought me an article on LDN (low-dose naltrexone). This use was new to me. Naltrexone is commonly used to treat opiate and alcohol dependency at 50-100 milligrams.

At low doses, three to four milligrams, for un-known reasons, treats pain and inflammation. I took a few days to read the evidence (it was lacking but showed promise) and followed up shortly after to let her know I was ready to initiate therapy using the LDN at lower doses and titrate upwards. I felt comfortable trying this for a couple of reasons: It was inexpensively produced at the local compounding pharmacy, and the side effect profile is so minimal, I figured, "Why not? Let's give it a go!"

Initially, she responded well, but her pain started returning. We titrated up one-half a milligram, and her pain reduced. We were hopeful this would take care of her problem. We continued to monitor and adjust the dose as needed, but to be honest, I didn't know if this would be the be-all-end-all of her therapy, so I tempered her expectations accordingly. "You may need to start prednisone or a DMARD," She understood and was grateful that I was willing to experiment and try the naltrexone.

This is a good example of balancing free thinking/clinical experience and EBM.

Like musicians who improvise their playing, sometimes doctors must as well. When musicians get together to *jam*, they often enter the room without knowing the music they are about to make. The drummer starts with a beat, followed by the bass player. Then maybe the guitarist follows with the keyboardist while watching the bass player to determine which key is being played on the spot—slowly improvising their way into a groove that sits *deep in the pocket, man*—that's musician talk!

A successful musical improv happens when musicians have honed their skill enough to know which chords or notes work in the key being played. Just as a good doctor will when they have honed their skill enough to honor the foundation (EBM/music theory), trust their instinct to think non-linearly (clinical experience/improvising), while doing no harm (keep your instruments tuned). This comes with experience, time, and inherent trust in your skills and knowledge.

POWER OF SUGGESTION

"You love this book."

— Dr. Michael Lewis

THE POWER OF SUGGESTION IS A POWERFUL tool in our arsenal. Just as the placebo effect can cause positive outcomes approximately 30% of the time, so can the power of positive thinking, especially when one is prompted via the power of suggestion. The mind is a powerful tool and one can convince themselves that a treatment works even if it's bogus.

Placebos are of the utmost importance in scientific studies, specifically randomized, double-blind, placebo-controlled studies. In these studies, participants are randomly placed into one of two groups, a control group (sugar-pill or placebo group) or a study group (therapy or medication group). To limit potential biases, neither the patients nor the researchers know who gets a placebo. This is to prevent bias from effecting results. This includes withholding that a placebo is part of the study.

In practice, the number one reason why a medication is discontinued within the first two weeks is abdominal discomfort. Usually, if people stick with it for another week or two, discomfort goes away, especially when providers *suggest* it will:

Marco was a 56-year-old male, well known to me, and coming in to follow up on his blood pressure medication. I previously started him on low-dose Lisinopril for multiple blood pressure elevations. He usually complained of nausea and constipation with numerous medications in the past but trusted me and heeded my advice. "Dr. Mike, ever since I started taking this pill, I've been feeling some abdominal cramping and excess gas," he stated. "So sorry, Marco. That's odd because this medication isn't known to cause this type of reaction. Have you been feeling well otherwise?" He states, "Yes, only since I started this medication." I thought, his blood pressure was a perfect 118/78, and I would hate to discontinue it too early. I said, "I'll tell you what, Marco, this medication shouldn't cause any more side effects. If it was the pill, abdominal reactions should only last one week—I want you to continue it for another two weeks. I'm sure you will be okay." "Okay, Dr. Mike. I trust you," he stated confidently. He returned two weeks later for a repeat blood pressure check without abdominal discomfort. He said, "You were correct, Dr. Mike. As soon as I left your office, my symptoms stopped."

While suggestibility and placebos can affect positive outcomes of specific therapies, the inverse is true as well. A *nocebo*, the red-headed step-child of placebo and suggestibility, is a harm-causing placebo. For example, if a patient is told that a therapy will likely cause side effects, recent objective findings using functional MRI (fMRI) images suggest this is true. In a study released in 2012, researchers asked, "Do expectations shape pain?" One section about nocebos stated:

One fMRI study examined nocebo effects using an acupuncture model. Subjects were led to believe that pain would increase with acupuncture to the meridian side of the arm. Sham acupuncture was applied, and responses to noxious heat on nocebo sites were compared to responses on control sites with no expectation. Nocebo treatment increased in the medial pain system, including the anterior cingulate cortex and bilateral insula. These effects are consistent with placebo effects reviewed above, though, as discussed below, the neuromodulatory mechanisms thought to underlie placebo and nocebo are quite distinct.

Do we need the fMRI to explain this? No, but objective evidence is important in understanding the complexity how the power of suggestion *looks* in our brain. Whether we are talking about the power of suggestion, placebos, or nocebos, the common thread woven between all three entities is the *mind*. Understanding how the power of suggestion influences responses to a presented stimulus should not be taken for granted when physicians or other healthcare practitioners treat their patients.

In this case, the mind is a terrible thing to . . . ignore.

PART FOUR

THE INTERFERENCE OF TRADITIONAL MODELS OF MEDICINE

H. M. O-No!

*"All the incentives are toward less medical care because
... the less care they give them, the more money they
make."*

— Edgar Kaiser (Permanente)

IF THE QUOTE ABOVE DIDN'T MAKE YOU GASP, I'm not sure what
will. Let's be clear. I believe in free-market capitalism. I
believe in the freedom to run your business as you like. I
support profits and non-profits. Yet I get outraged when
medical groups and organizations, such as the one listed
above, market taglines like: "Because health isn't an
industry. It's a cause," yet treat patients like cattle. I
understand our healthcare system is in turmoil and
under insurmountable pressure to provide affordable
care, but the resources aren't there. Rant starts here: We
have more people shoved into a system that is already
overcrowded. This, in turn, overwhelms the system,
decreases access to care, decreases time spent face-to-
face with the doctor and patient, increases wait times,

and increases the risk of harm, all the while burning out the physician and leading them to leave the organization thus adding to a worsening access problem. Their foresight sucks.

The HMO model is like a copy machine. You feed the paper in (patients), it goes through the scanner (physician) and spits you out on the other side (visit complete). As in the copy world, the more PPM (pages per minute) one machine accomplishes, the better it appears to be. Sometimes, the paper jams (*this patient requires more time*), and the system halts (*increased wait times*), requiring you to dismantle and reset the system (*physician problem solving*). Once the jam is dislodged (*problem dealt with*), the PPM gets back on track (*next patient*):

> *Cynthia was a 49-year-old female who was scheduled for a 15-minute visit to discuss her back pain. I walked through the door and noticed something felt off. "Hi Cynthia . . . How are you?" "I'm okay, my back is acting up again, and I was wondering if you can help me." "I'm so sorry, I hope so," I said confidently. We spent some time talking, checking her chart, and examining her. Before I was ready to wrap up, I looked at her eyes and noticed a lot of sadness. "Cynthia, what's going on . . . you okay? You look . . . heavy." Immediately, she*

broke down crying (paper jam). "Dr. Lewis, I'm so sad; last week I lost my father . . . I've been so depressed and sad; I haven't done much."

I heard the rattling of the vital sign cart rolling into the next room as my next patient awaited my arrival (system halts). Cynthia continued, "I've pretty much been in my bed for four days and was barely able to gather the energy to go to the funeral, but that's it." It's evident that Cynthia needed someone, and I'm glad it was me, just to be an ear and a source of support. We had a back and forth for about 15 minutes while the rattling wheels of the vital sign machine followed yet, another patient into the next room (system severely halted). Cynthia seemed to have perked up a bit, and we laughed a little. She said, "Oh my God, I can't believe how much time I've taken . . . You must be so behind." I replied, "Cynthia, this is where I want to be. If I were only interested in time, I wouldn't have inquired. You are my priority right now, and I'm grateful you trusted me enough to open up." I hugged her and told her to come back anytime, even if just to talk and process (paper jam resolved).

In medicine, especially in fast-paced organizations, many see patients' tears as time consumers as opposed to an invitation. Many doctors have a lot of judgment about emotional complaints or mental health visits. Unfortunately, this sentiment is pervasive in healthcare. Yes, these visits take more time. Yes, they can be frustrating, especially on a hectic day with multiple paper jams, but so be it. We are here to heal and minimize suffering. We must make room in our bloated schedule to tend to it the best we can.

Thinking solely about time doesn't necessarily mean a physician lacks compassion (though it may), but due to the fast-paced system they work in, time also becomes a priority. I don't believe patients themselves burn out the physicians; the problem is too many patients and too little time.

If I'm being honest, after seeing Cynthia, I was hoping that the subsequent two patients waiting for me only had something like a sore throat—quick and easy. I was honored to be part of Cynthia's process; thinking about time was just being pragmatic. However, checking our watch, rushing our patients, or giving them only one or two concerns to discuss severely hinders the rapport, relationship, and connection.

This is a system-wide problem, not only within HMOs but with most doctors who are part of the traditional, insurance-based system. With insurance reimbursements decreasing, doctors and organizations have no choice but to see herds of people daily to keep the revenue coming in to support their families, pay off student loans, staff, keep up with equipment leases, and rent so patients have a place to be seen. As I said, it's a system-wide problem without a simple answer. With fewer physicians entering primary care and tens of millions of new patients entering the system, the *Unaffordable* Care Act (*un*ACA) has caused a worsening bottleneck.

Physician access is limited, as already mentioned, and many HMOs don't take the plans that the patient used to have before the *un*ACA came into action. So, even if the patient was seeing the same doctor for 15 years and there was rapport and a connection, if the provider isn't on one of the selected plans, the patient loses their trusted confidant. The patient must reestablish with a new doctor or change their current plan.

Another one bites the dust.

Pie Anyone?

"I'll gladly pay you Tuesday for a hamburger today."

— Wimpy (from the cartoon *Popeye*)

IN THE 19TH CENTURY, DOCTORS received payment for procedures performed. It was a fee-for-service model like today's medical practice. However, in the 1800s, bartering was common using whatever produce, pies, services, or goods were available.[14]

Physicians were respected and among the community's most important members, especially in early frontier communities. Doctors weren't wealthy; they earned maybe $10-20 per week. It's been said:

"Doctors traveled long distances on foot, horseback, in wagons, buggies, ferries, canoes, and boats. Traveling to a settlement might be a cross-country journey on nothing more than an unmarked trail. The doctor's bag was designed to carry the tools of the trade and withstand travel in all sorts of weather. Bags of durable

oiled canvas or leather stood up to extended travel, whatever the season and terrain. Rural doctors were general practitioners by necessity. They delivered babies, set broken limbs, pulled teeth, and tended to all sorts of wounds and diseases. They often carried medications and many of the instruments they used. The rural family doctor was well known in the community and was often considered the most valuable asset in the area. They most probably delivered every child in the community and sat with the dying as they drew their last breath. They saw people in and out of this world and tried to keep them alive and healthy."[15]

There have been great medical advances since then, from washing hands in 1847 to organ transplantation in 1954 and sequencing the human genome in 2003.

While medical advances are positive, it seems we have moved away from the simplicity of the doctor-patient relationship.

Living expenses are rising dramatically causing many doctors to focus on making ends meet, shifting focus away from when patients were the priority.

Many people can't afford insurance, and no large organization will see them without payment up-front. They are then forced to go to local county hospitals where they may wait eight hours to be seen. While hardship coverage may help to pay for some things, these patients may still be responsible for a significant portion of the cost.

Back when I owned my direct primary care practice, patients would say, "Dr. Mike, you've gone back to the way medicine used to be, if only I could afford your services." I might tell them, "Thank you, maybe we can discuss alternative payments . . .

Do you bake?"

Blowing Smoke
Up Your Ass

"If you believe that, I have a bridge to sell you."

— Unknown, based on George C. Parker

MANY ALTERNATIVE PRACTITIONERS seem to think that detoxifying the body via the rectum is *the* great cure-all. From colonics to coffee-enemas to the sham, expensive Gerson institute in Tijuana, Mexico, apparently ridding your body of shit cures cancer.

With the advent of complementary medicine and a growing number of disenchanted patients, it's no surprise that some nefarious entities are capitalizing on this segment of the population.

Around the 1770s, doctors started using tobacco as an adjunct to regular healing practices such as leech therapy and bloodletting—you know, the "typical stuff." Classically, Native Americans used sage, tobacco, and cedar to heal their community. Unfortunately, non-natives, specifically the British, perverted these traditions and started using them for healing in strange ways. I assume they thought if sage and tobacco had great healing powers when passed over a patient, then blowing it inside of one would be even better. So, that's what they did. This became the origin of the term, *"blowing smoke up your ass."* It was thought this procedure would help resuscitate people who were near-drowning or drowned:

Smoke was literally blown up the rectum by inserting a tube. This tube was connected to a fumigator and a bellows, which forced smoke into the rectum. Sometimes a more direct route to the lungs was taken by forcing the smoke into the nose and mouth, but most physicians felt the rectal method was more effective. The nicotine in tobacco was thought to stimulate the heart to beat stronger and faster, thus encouraging respiration. The smoke was also thought to warm the victim and dry out the person's insides, removing excessive moisture. [16]

They believed in the power of this intervention so much, they put it along major waterways such as the River Thames in London. I guess you can call it the original AED (automatic external defibrillator) that you see hanging on the walls of airports to help revive a person in cardiac arrest.

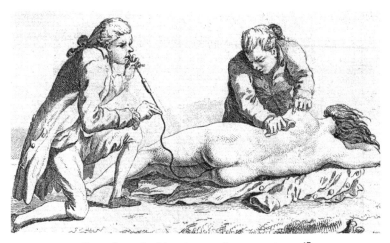

Procedure for blowing smoke up one's ass [17]

Given that our current healthcare crisis has led to higher copays and premiums, many frustrated and disenchanted patients are seeking alternative treatments: Essential oils, naturopaths, chiropractors, reiki therapists, and acupuncturists, to name a few. I have used and advocated most of these modalities and found them beneficial. In fact, I myself am a level-one reiki healer, and used some Native American traditional healing in my practice, including meditation and smudging with sage.

Thinking outside the box broadens our scope of knowledge and allows us to expand our healing repertoire. There is a faction of doctors who don't believe in CAM (complementary and alternative medicine) because they are purists (to put it lightly). When I think about these purists, I imagine a Caesar-esque individual, soap-boxing to a crowd of thousands in a large amphitheater, throwing his upwardly placed fist into the air, donning a tuxedo and a monocle shouting in a king's tone:

> *"There cannot be a complement to allopathic medicine . . . This <air quotes> CAM is hyperbole at best. Medicine is a world unto itself. We stand tall on the shoulders of our predecessors, and we will not be fallen to fakery, quackery, or tomfoolery. We are the saviors! We are life's knights in shining armor! We are doctors! So be it!"*
>
> *The crowd roars.*

Too far?

CAM can have significant benefits when dealing with anxiety because the focus isn't on prescription medications. Yoga, mindfulness training, and meditation are all excellent means to help calm anxiety symptoms but aren't root-cause cures. Though herbs and other homeopathic remedies, such as St. John's Wort, are common in the "natural" treatment of anxiety and depression, there are potential side effects related to blocking the monoamine oxidase system (the biochemical pathway of this herb). Though some people may have benefited from using them, these herbs are not regulated by the FDA, thus likely having dosing issues, which can be less safe than a prescription. But, if one is interested in dealing with their anxiety or depression, looking beyond symptom control may be the best bet.

Though I believe there are many well-intentioned alternative medicine providers and practices, there are many that pray on peoples' anxiety to build their business.

The awareness of our mortality manifests in all sorts of ways, most of which is outside of our awareness. Feeling anxicty is normal in life. Fearing death or contemplating your own death (not necessarily suicide, but not excluding it either) are normal thoughts we have as human beings as well.

Dr. Irvin Yalom, Ph.D., author of Staring at the Sun: Overcoming the Terror of Death, believes that the fear of death is at the heart of much of our anxiety. He writes:

Why, you may ask, take on this unpleasant, frightening subject? Why stare into the sun? Why not follow the advice of the venerable dean of American psychiatry, Adolph Meyer, who, a century ago, cautioned psychiatrists, 'Don't scratch where it doesn't itch?' Why grapple with the most terrible, the darkest and most unchangeable aspect of life? . . . Death, however, DOES itch. It itches all the time; it is always with us, scratching at some inner door, whirring softly, barely audibly, just under the membrane of consciousness.

Death anxiety can manifest as anxiety and worry from a basic sore throat to a painful toe. Preoccupation with health is often an indicator of unexamined issues relating to mortality. For example, *Globus Hystericus* is a common diagnosis (which still bears a pejorative name) where one feels a lump in their throat not caused by anything physical. It is a common sensation, which tricks many doctors into following the scent of the red herrings. Some people become so frustrated that a physician can't find the *physical* cause of their problem (not just globus hystericus) that they scour the internet until they find a diagnosis that fits their symptoms:

Kelly was a 19-year-old female who came to see me because she had been complaining of "not feeling well" for some time. She was generally healthy with a self-reported history of OCD and depression. She came to my office for an initial consultation with her parents to see if I could help her, as she has been to four other doctors in the past that she "didn't like" and disagreed with their diagnoses (red flag!). She told me she was infected with parasites and was taking this parasite-killing herb, which worked initially but "didn't get them all." She told me she was tired and didn't feel like herself. She was taking multiple natural herbs from internet sites, all of which were "validated" by "real-life" testimonials of people who shit out cups of parasites after taking this concoction—these sites always show "wormy"-poo in a cup. Gross. Kelly also discussed tiny fibers coming out of her skin, which were "definitely parasites."

I closely reviewed her symptoms checklist. "I see you marked OCD and depression. How is that going?" "Okay. I'm feeling just fine," she said apathetically. Her parents, concerned for her physical well-being, colluded with her. There wasn't much mention of her emotional state (I would guess for fear of minimizing her symptoms). She had been reading internet sites that were validating her symptoms. I said, "That's horrible. Have you been tested for parasites?" She said, "No." "Why not?" I asked curiously. "I just never did." "Okay, that'll be the first thing we do because parasites are very difficult to get, especially when you haven't been to the tropics or out of the country."

She then continued to tell me about her fatigue and how her thyroid was the culprit. She firmly said, "I know my thyroid is not right, Dr. Mike. I've been told my TSH and T4 are fine, but the T3 has never been measured." She paused for a moment. She continued, "You know how the thyroid works, don't you? It · controls everything from digestion to fatigue. It's an organ located in the . . ." I thought, "Seriously?" I interrupted, "Yes, I know how the thyroid works, thank you. I will be happy to check that too." We ended the meeting and she returned for blood work and to pick up a stool collection kit to check for the tests we discussed.

A week went by, and all her results returned negative. Her thyroid tests (TSH, free T4, and free T3, which she wanted) were perfectly normal. Her microscopic stool studies were completely normal. When she came to see me, I told her the good news. She seemed happy, I guess, but still quite skeptical of the results. She said, "Sometimes when people take these herbs to kill the parasites, they say that the parasite testing can be wrong." <sigh> "Well," I said, "This is as definitive as we are going to get. I hear you are frustrated. Sometimes we need to look other places if we have done the proper tests, don't find anything, and continue to have symptoms. You mentioned you had OCD and depression. Do you think this may be related to how you feel?" I asked. "I am depressed because of my symptoms, look, can I still take the natural thyroid supplement because I'm sure the tests are wrong." I said, "I don't *recommend it, but if you wish, go ahead. Just call me should you have any problems, and we can check your thyroid tests in 6 weeks."*

Not two hours later, she called, and she fired me. She was pissed. "Dr. Lewis, I think your tests are wrong, I think you are incompetent, and I know you think I'm crazy." I told her, "I am sorry I couldn't help you, but I'm here for you should you need anything." She hung up. I refunded her fees and never heard from her again.

Kelly had significant mental health issues manifesting in her symptoms. Unfortunately, she wasn't with me long enough to establish a better rapport so we could delve deeper into what was happening beneath the surface. I knew she had delusional parasitism (*Morgellon's disease*), and no herb or test would make her feel better. Many websites prey on people's anxieties and perpetuate their illness for profit. I understood why she fired her four previous doctors.

Patients like Kelly will find an alternative healer who may put them on expensive and frequent herbal "remedies" to "cleanse" the "toxins" from their "vessel," or they will continue to show up multiple times per week at your office looking for answers. When this occurs, it is our duty as physicians to ask, to confront, and to educate patients about the connection between the mind and the body. For doctors or other clinical staff to label them as "crazy" is unfortunately a common practice, especially in emergency settings.

Few things are more distasteful than calling someone "crazy" who is suffering from psychosomatic symptoms. Sitting with them without judgment is important. Curiosity and compassion can go a long way in establishing the trust necessary for exploring underlying emotional issues.

I know it's tough, but I have faith in you.

IT'S A BIRD. IT'S A PLANE. IT'S SUPERBUGS!

"Gimme a whiskey, ginger ale on the side, and don't be stingy, baby!"

— Greta Garbo as Anna Christie

WITH RISING HEALTHCARE COSTS many frustrated patients' have expectations about what they want even before they walk into the office. Many patients want something *tangible* to treat their ailments—regardless of its appropriateness. "Go home, take two aspirins, and call me in the morning" doesn't work well for this group. A common scenario is when a patient demands an antibiotic for a simple "cold," after a day or two of symptoms. Even when the reality is that most "colds" do not respond to antibiotics 90% of the time. Unfortunately, providers accommodate these requests for multiple reasons. While on the surface this seems benign, there is a staggering increase in superbugs causing significant morbidity (illness) and mortality (death). Listed below are some of the most common superbugs:

> Methicillin-resistant Staphylococcus aureus (MRSA)
> Vancomycin-resistant Enterococcus (VRE)
> ESBL-producing Enterobacteriaceae (extended-spectrum β-lactamases)
> Multidrug-resistant Pseudomonas aeruginosa
> Carbapenem-resistant Enterobacteriaceae (CRE)
> Multidrug-resistant Acinetobacter

Superbugs are an evolved group of bacteria that have been exposed to an increased number of antibiotics, leading them to develop a resistance over time. Antibiotic resistance occurs when bacteria develop "immunity" after prolonged exposure to antibiotics.

The reasons why medical providers are over-prescribing antibiotics aren't necessarily clear. I believe there are multiple issues at play from patient satisfaction, office-visit time restraints, and rising copays, to name a few. Educating our patients and giving them a rationale about the decisions to use antibiotics can help eliminate the patient's frustration when an antibiotic isn't inappropriate:

José was a pleasant 38-year-old gentleman who came

to the urgent care where I was working with a chief complaint of a *"sore throat."* I walked in and introduced myself, *"Good evening, José, what's going on?"* He replied, *"Doc, I've had this sore throat for two days and it's really knocking me down."* He rubbed his nose, *"I'm tired and have nasal congestion."* I asked, *"Do you have any other symptoms?"* He stated, *"No."* I responded, *"Oh man, I'm so sorry."* I examined him and then stated, *"Okay, José, I'm gonna take good care of you, buddy. I don't think you need an antibiotic today, but I do believe . . ."* He interrupted, *"Doc, I really need an antibiotic, every time I get one, I feel better."*

At this point, I could roll my eyes and conclude the visit, or I could teach. I chose to teach. *"I hear you, José. When I determine if I need to use an antibiotic, I think of these statistics. Picture this: If I had 100 adults in a room with sore throats, I could immediately remove about 90 because research shows us that a virus causes their illness. That leaves 10 people, correct?"* He nods. I continue, *"The 10 people left over have a sore throat that is likely caused by bacteria. Out of these 10, nine of them are due to the bacteria Streptococcus or, as you know it, strep. So, we can perform a rapid strep test, and if it's negative, I can remove the nine people to join the other 90, and we can logically deduce that your sore throat is 99% due to a virus; therefore, we don't need an*

antibiotic. Let's let the strep test decide for us, shall we?"
He nodded and said, "Great. That makes sense."

Many doctors may have given José the antibiotics; however, recognizing the opportunity to soothe his anxiety about his illness by teaching, building rapport, and gaining trust was more valuable.

The strep test returned negative, and José was pleased. He left the office, thanked me for helping him, and went on his way without complaint.

PATIENT SATISFACTION SCORES

My theory is that patient satisfaction scores are loosely associated with the rising superbug epidemic. In large organizations such as HMOs bonuses depend on many areas, from meeting preventive health goals to increasing patient volume and, most importantly, patient satisfaction scores. These scores are usually generated based on random surveys from the physician's patient pool. From the answers given, doctors are ranked amongst their peers. At the end of the year, or quarterly, or whatever the organization decides, bonuses are handed out to shareholders of the company—the better scores, the more money one would receive. The opposite holds true as well.

OFFICE VISIT TIME RESTRAINTS

Rushed visits are not uncommon, especially in urgent care settings and high-volume medical offices. Urgent care centers are *solution* focused, which may be a factor in overprescribing antibiotics.

RISING COPAYS

Due to rising copays, insurance companies have a passive responsibility for the superbug epidemic. While a direct correlation can't be made between rising copays and overprescribing antibiotics, it's an important variable in the matrix of what influences decisions.

G.O.M.E.R.S. (Get Out of My Emergency Room)

Mark, 36, and his wife Peg, 35, arrived in my urgent care complaining of sore throats for the last two days. "Hi guys, what can I do for you today?" Mark replied, "We've had a sore throat for a day or so and wanted to get checked out." I proceeded to ask the basic questions and obtain a good history from them. I said, "You likely don't have strep throat and don't need an antibiotic, but I would be happy . . ." I was interrupted as all facades of niceties faded on their end. Mark said, "First of all,

I'm not leaving here without an antibiotic. Period. That's why we came here. So, what are you gonna do?" I interjected, "Sure, I understand that. Let's do a strep test to ascertain whether you do or don't require it." I gave my speech on sore throat statistics. Mark yelled, "All of you are alike. You just want me to spend money so you can pad your pockets." I said calmly, "Look, I'm happy to take care of both of you, but I want to do it properly, in fact, since you both have a similar illness, let me at least test one of you . . . take it or leave it." He agreed to the test, and I left the room so the medical assistant (MA) could come in and do the testing. From the other room, I heard him raise his voice. The MA came out and said, "He yelled at me and was so rude to me." I said, "Is that so!" I walked over to their exam room, opened the door and didn't give anyone a chance to explain. "It's time you leave. I don't appreciate how you spoke to my staff. You're not welcome here. There's another urgent care across the street, we will refund your copay at the front." I left the room.

Two hours later, I received a negative Yelp review from Mark. He also mentioned how he went across the street to the other urgent care who gave him an antibiotic because *they knew what they were doing,* and I was incompetent. For many private physicians, their best business referrals are local reviews. It's not difficult to imagine how the fear of negative reviews can alter ones prescribing habits.

The irony is, I have often given a prescription for an antibiotic to fill in seven days if they worsen or don't improve, saving them another trip/copay.

One caveat: I don't do favors for assholes.

PROGNOSIS, NEGATIVE

"As I grew a little older and wiser I realized that unlike the fairy tales I had read as a child, the rabbit holes of the real world were often our own mad hearts."

— Beau Taplin

IF WE CONTINUE ON THE SAME MEDICAL PATH, medicine won't be dissimilar to buying a sandwich or going to the mechanic. There are reasons people have had the same doctor for years. This is because there's usually a mutually caring relationship. In our current health*care* climate, with so many limitations, red tape, bureaucracy, micromanagement, costs, time constraints, corporate demands, insurance intrusions, and confusion, it seems like an impossibility to establish a long-term caring relationship with your physician. We have been losing more primary care physicians every year, while insurance carriers are backing out of the Unaffordable Care Act exchanges due to loss in revenues. I fear that the system will fall further down the rabbit hole if significant changes don't happen soon.

Many doctors would love to break out of the bureaucratic system and do something else with their career, but don't know where to go. What's different at that clinic around the corner compared to this clinic? The frustrations about time, salary, micromanagement, insurance companies, and regulations all exist in most insurance-based clinics leaving many doctors feeling trapped. Trust me, I really understand that! I used to be one of them until I couldn't take it anymore.

I had enough.

Patients continue to be frustrated as the number of family doctors dwindle. New doctors aren't matriculating into primary care residencies like they used to. The current reality of less pay and more work is probably the reason. It's no secret that the system undervalues frontline medicine (primary care physicians) and is losing good doctors yearly. Pediatricians, psychiatrists, family practice, and internists are the lowest paid on the medical totem pole. Doctors are overwhelmed, frustrated, pushed to the limit, *and* still expected to give excellent patient care in seven minutes. It's atrocious, but it is a significant reason why the patient-doctor relationship is deteriorating. According to a study in the *Annals of Family Medicine* in 2020, improved physician-patient relationships showed a statistically significant change associated with im-proved functional health. Conversely, as the physician-patient relationships deteriorated, so did functional health.[18]

It's arrogant of the big medical corporations to preach corporate "feel-good" taglines such as "best patient care" and "patients come first" while they run their doctors into the ground allowing patient care to suffer. It's egregious. When are we going to pull the plug on this terminally ill system? I think *Seinfeld* explains it best:

The front door buzzes in Jerry's apartment, and Elaine pushes the button to talk.

Elaine: "Yeah?"

George: (mimicking a robot voice referring to the movie they are going to see) "Prognosis, Negative."

PART
FIVE

THE IMPORTANCE
OF SELF-CARE

The Person in the Mirror Wants You to Care

"If you have never seen a masterpiece, look in the mirror."

— Matshona Dhliwayo

MANY YEARS BACK, I STARTED A PATH of self-discovery. Though I was psychologically minded and curious, many parts of me were under-nurtured. My past struggles didn't get the attention they needed and were wreaking havoc in my personal and professional life. The fact is, it wasn't until early in my current relationship (now marriage), that those issues came to a head. As for many, relationship issues usually mirror family of origin dynamics, so it's difficult to see them when you are single.

It's a sad reality when you realize that it's the most important relationships in our lives that suffer the consequences of our unexamined past.

How do you ruin a marriage, find yourself in a family feud, and almost get fired from a job all in the same year? Answer: *Ignore* yourself. It was a tough time. All I knew was bad shit was happening around me, and I was an active participant in the process—silent masochism at its finest. My wife, Jenn, was working on her dissertation to earn her Ph.D. in clinical psychology and thought it would be a good idea for me to see a therapist. We were going through our own difficulties, so I knew her recommendation to see a therapist wasn't totally altruistic. However, she didn't offer the classic finger-pointing pejorative, "You need therapy!" It was a genuinely supportive request, as she saw my suffering and the effects it was having on me, in particular. I eventually agreed, made an appointment, and can still recall just how deeply moving my first appointment was with Dr. A. Let's just say, I was shaken to the core. I continued for a couple more months before I (prematurely) stopped.

Nonetheless, I was feeling better but still had lots of work to do on myself. Later, early in my third year of residency, I had a tough time focusing. I was making simple mistakes (non-life threatening), so much so, that the residency program director asked me if I was on drugs! I was so focused on a struggling marriage, a nuclear family back home that was in gridlock, and feelings of inadequacy that I had trouble focusing on my work. I *wasn't* on drugs. I was in pain, and only one man from a group of mentors, staff, elders, and directors inquired about my life, Dr. T. Once the director learned I wasn't on drugs, he tried to pathologize me by sending me to see someone for an ADD (attention deficit disorder) evaluation. I was in disbelief, I thought, "Drugs or pathology? Not even one question about my life."

In response to my "poor" showing at work, I was put into a weekly review course with Dr. T, a loving, academic man who knew that I was *good enough* well before I did. He always had my best interests at heart and felt I should go through the assessments as recommended because even if they were wrong, he said, "What's the worst that can happen?" So, I was sent for an ADD assessment with a local therapist. It was a fortuitous meeting. During my first ADD assessment with my new therapist, he just "got" me within the first 10 minutes. He said, "You don't have ADD, but for the hell of it, go online here [gave me a website address] and take the self-assessment, then let me know how you did." I didn't have ADD. I started doing more work with this therapist and made terrific strides in my healing and confidence. After four to six months or so, things at work were improving, I was feeling better, and Jenn and I were on a mending path. After residency I continued my inner work and saw the amazing value of therapy.

My work in therapy ebbed and flowed through low and high points in my life. After moving back home from residency, I started to see a psychologist, Dr. R., a very talented therapist who brought me to depths I wasn't even aware were there. With him, I graduated from psychological snorkeling to scuba diving. In our last session he mentioned, "You know Mike, you would do well in a men's group." I was intrigued and put it on the back burner for about a month or so, until I heard his words echo in my head. I started looking up local men's groups on the internet and found what would become a profound chapter of my life: Men's Center Los Angeles, Sacred Path Retreats with Dr. Stephen Johnson.

I attended my first retreat in 2013 and was eventually voted into the Wisdom Council (a group of men who prepare, arrange, and set up the retreats) and eventually to Associate Director of Retreats in 2016. These retreats gave me the strength, confidence, and courage to face the fears and issues that were holding me back and causing my relationships to suffer—especially the one with myself. If not for the retreat community, a courageous wife with the patience of a saint, and in-laws that saw beyond the pain and encouraged Jenn to wait it out, I wouldn't have been able to experience the inner joy and peace that I feel now. Yet, self-awareness came with its own challenges—the reminder of my own mortality and the transientness of all things.

Irvin Yalom discusses the paradoxical gift of self-awareness in his book, *Staring at the Sun: Overcoming the Terror of Death*:

> *Self-awareness is a supreme gift, a treasure as precious as life. This is what makes us human. But it comes with a costly price: the wound of mortality. Our existence is forever shadowed by the knowledge that we will grow, blossom, and, inevitably, diminish and die.*

I realized I wasn't able use my gift to its full capacity in my practice until I genuinely cared for myself and dealt with some hard truths. Now that there is psychological room within myself, I can be there for my patients on a deeper level; and though it takes more time, the benefits are worth it. So, when I speak with men and women in my practice who are struggling with their jobs, anxiety, depression, sexual dysfunction, chronic pain, morbid obesity, anger issues, and so forth, I am better able to help sherpa them through their difficulties onto a healing path.

I encourage everyone to face hard truths, look inwards and make yourself a priority. *Every* relationship will improve, including the one with yourself. It's natural to feel apprehensive, I feel you.

In the words of Dr. T, "What's the worst that can happen?"

TIME TO CHECK IN ...
WITH YOURSELF

"We're sorry; you have reached a number that has been disconnected or is no longer in service. If you feel you have reached this recording in error, please check the number and try your call again."

— Phone intercept message

WE LIVE IN A DISCONNECTED WORLD filled with many distractions. Ironically, the things that supposedly connect us (computers, cell phones, social media) may be contributing to our alienation from others. When we are so focused on things external, we can lose contact with our inner selves.

We spend unprecedented amounts of time looking for answers outside of ourselves, when in fact, everything we need resides within us. Many seek to fill their emptiness through short-lived happiness acquired through nicer cars or bigger houses. While those things make most of us feel good in the short term; it will inevitably fade, and the cycle begins again.

What happens when we depend on external means to validate our worth and define our identity? The minute we get there, whether it be a dollar amount in the bank account, the big promotion, etc. we find that we are no more fulfilled than when we started. It can be a devastating realization.

Finding true contentment and growth require *active* processes of introspection. Let's face it, we all carry around some amount of baggage that directs our behavior in one direction or another outside of our awareness. We regain our power when we examine our internal world and take the reins from our subconscious.

Most of us think we've got our shit together and don't need therapy. I've been there. The reality is most people don't seek help until the *shit hits the fan*, as it did for me. So, keep your eyes peeled for flying shit!

A positive side-effect of self-examination is less reactivity and more curiosity. The most important question we can ask ourselves is, "What is my reaction saying about me?" My father-in-law, Tom talks about emotional reactivity in a way that has always resonated with me:

It appears the majority of people, when reacting to the slings and arrows of existence, do not even stop to think about why they are reacting to them the way they do. The result is that they are on to their next reaction in the same way. Why is this ineffective? It is the harm to oneself and others it can do. I liken it to pinball, where the ball careens from pillar to post in a random, if not chaotic way, to its ultimate demise. Granted, judicious use of the flippers can delay the inevitable, but most folks do not even avail themselves metaphorically of that. The consequence is that things can get out of hand with oneself and with other people. It seems that one's initial reaction to some stress event, which all of us have, must be internally reviewed before acting on that initial reaction. Unfortunately, this does not happen for most people, so it is on to the next reaction like a pinball and leads to unwanted psychological and interpersonal problems.

Human beings tend to be reactive, not proactive when it comes to our mental health, correct? In relationships, isn't it easier to point fingers at our *opponents* (spouse, boss, lover, etc.) than to take an honest look at ourselves? Where does that get us? How did *we* contribute to the issues at hand? To grow, we must point the fingers back at ourselves, courageously and compassionately. In my own experience, without this type of introspection, my relationships would continue to be riddled with defensiveness, anger, resentment, frustration, sadness, and loneliness.

When I talk to patients about grief, depression, low self-worth, or anxiety, I come from a humanistic perspective rather than just regurgitating information written in textbooks.

As physicians, I believe the quality of our patient care improves when we care for ourselves first.

Except for first responders, few professions in this world have witnessed life and death as physicians do. Stillbirths, traumatic amputations, gun-shot victims, family members losing their last living relative, listening to the last heartbeat of a dying patient, the eerie silence of the body without breath or heartbeat, crying with a spouse who just lost their partner, delivering a baby with anencephaly (no skull-cap), or feeling so overworked from a 32-hour shift that you couldn't even put a sentence together, are just a few examples.

Witnessing these profound moments changes you.

Shit, if anyone needs some emotional support, I think it's providers, don't you? It's a well-known fact that physicians are horrible patients, and God forbid we acknowledge that we have "emotional problems," right?

Some providers would say, "I've become accustomed to death, and it doesn't bother me anymore." However, what is masquerading as apathy is in fact an adaptative strategy to cope with the horrors of the job. While this coping mechanism is necessary to function at work, it's important to process and work through vicarious trauma so as not to let it bleed into other areas of one's life.

I'M OK? YOU'RE OK?

"You are not your illness. You have an individual story to tell. You have a name, a history, a personality. Staying yourself is part of the battle."

— Julian Seifter, MD

ERVING HOFFMAN DEFINES STIGMA as "a process by which the reaction of others spoils normal identity." Seeking help when needed is always a good idea. We are all flawed and have parts of our personality that make tolerating us a little challenging. Flaws are things that we would label as problem issues with ourselves. Often times, these flaws are out of our awareness, met with denial or defensiveness, when pointed out.

To be flawed is to be human. These flaws can present opportunities to grow and learn more about ourselves.

A blind spot, by definition, is a lack of insight or awareness—often persistent—about a specific area of one's behavior. The only way to know we have one is if someone points it out—to our dismay.

The defense mechanisms we develop in childhood, eventually outlive their usefulness. In my case, my defensiveness masked deep insecurities and shame.

But what if you were able to rise above the negative-self talk (I'm not good enough) and defensiveness (It's not my issue, it's yours!) and examine it without judgment? We may learn something about ourselves. If we have the courage to face ourselves and *not* self-medicate we may realize our full potential.

Stepping out of one's comfort zone is difficult, scary and takes a lot of courage. Facing our issues requires a great deal of motivation. For me, my motivation was my family, my work, my principles, and my integrity. What's yours?

I wish I would've nipped my issues in the bud before hitting bottom, but I've gained enough wisdom to know that we don't change until we are ready—not a moment before.

Though the stigma or apprehensiveness of therapy crosses all genders and sexes, women are better at asking for help. This doesn't mean that all women are great at expressing themselves, nor should it be an excuse for *stoic* men not to express their feelings. In my life, I've been lucky to be in the presence of men that easily express themselves—they didn't get there without having to confront their own issues and societal gender norms. I've also been fortunate to know many good women who struggled because of their socio-cultural backgrounds. Ambivalence about seeking help is an issue many of us struggle with and is heavily influenced by gender and societal norms, religion, ethnicity, genetics and culture:

Josefina was a 46-year-old Mexican female who came to see me because she was having trouble sleeping. I walked into the exam room, and I could already feel the energy emanating from her pores; her hair was somewhat disheveled, and she looked tired. "Hi Josefina! It's nice to see you again. What's going on?" She replied, "Oh doctor, I'm having such trouble sleeping. I'm up all night. I need something for sleep doctor." "Why? What's going on?" I responded. "I don't know, doctor. I just don't sleep. I've been crying all the time." "How is work, Josefina?" "Okay, doctor." "How are things at home?" I asked softly. "Stressful doctor," she started crying. I sat down on my stool, rolled over to her and put my hand on hers, "What's happening?" I said looking directly into her eyes. "It's my husband doctor, we are thinking of getting a divorce." "Why?" I asked gently. "He just tells me he doesn't want to be married to me anymore." She put her face in her hands and cried. I gave her a tissue. We spent the next 10 or 15 minutes talking about their marriage's dynamics and how she felt. I asked, "Have you ever seen a therapist?" "Why doctor, I'm not crazy."

I chuckled, "Of course not Josefina, but sometimes when we are going through a tough time, it's nice to have someone to help us who isn't related to the problem at all. A neutral third party." "Oh doctor, I'm not crazy, I don't need therapy." "I hear you, Josefina. I know you are not crazy, but it sounds like you could use some support," I said as I rolled my stool backward. She responded, "In my country, doctor, we don't do that. We keep it in family." "Okay, so have you talked to your family about this?" I asked. "No, I don't want to burden my family, doctor."

I thought, "But what about the 'we keep it in the family' thing?" So, I said, "It seems that your family isn't a source of help for you at this time, so let me give you a recommendation for a therapist, and should you want some help maneuvering through this hard time, please reach out." She nodded, "Okay, doctor." I rolled forward again, closer to her, and said, "Josefina, it's normal to have ups and downs in your life and I'm so sorry you are going through this, it sounds very painful. I have had my own ups and downs too and have seen a therapist. Please remember that you deserve to help *yourself and don't have to do this alone. Seeking help isn't weakness, Josefina. And remember, you were strong enough to make an appointment with me today. I hope you take my recommendation.*

There are many misconceptions about psychotherapy. Generationally speaking, during The Depression, the parents of the baby-boomers (The traditionalists) were focused on survival—putting food on the table—there wasn't space for addressing mental health.

As a physician, having an awareness of our patients' unique background and socio-cultural influences may help us when initiating conversations about mental health.

I had good outcomes when normalizing presenting issues and destigmatizing therapy. This helps address their shame and reminds them that their suffering is not unique to them.

Opening a dialogue and encouraging them to reach out to their support system is key. I think it's essential to seek help, and if that's in the confines of the family, church, synagogue, or mosque, so be it. However, if the status quo isn't working, perhaps it's time to challenge those norms and seek outside help. We owe it to ourselves and our loved ones.

Rigid ideals of masculinity have been so deeply ingrained in men, they may associate seeking support with weakness or failure. This is especially evident with issues pertaining to sexual dysfunction.

John was a 33-year-old man who came to my office to discuss "sexual problems." Following our greeting, he looked down and bashfully said, "Hi doctor, I'm having some ... I don't know, issues, you know ..." He paused. Given is chief complaint and body language, "Erection issues?" I asked. "Yes," he said. "What's the problem? Staying hard or getting hard?" (Most men usually appreciate a direct question). He chuckled, "Both." "Okay, and does it happen all the time, John?" "No, but it's frequent. Sometimes it's like [hits his fist into his hand a couple of times], you know? Other times I just can't perform [simulates a flaccid penis with his index finger], and it's driving my girlfriend nuts. She thinks I'm not into her." "Are you?" I asked. "What?" he asked, confused, "Into her?" I said. "Yes, doc, I am." "Okay good, at least that's not the problem. So, when did this start, John? When was the first time this happened?" A few seconds passed as he thought back and replied, "I think I was about 22 years old and I was having sex with my new girlfriend, and I lost it doc. I just lost my hard-on. I guess it was because I was stressed at work or something." "How did she handle it?" I asked. He shook his head back and forth and said, "Man, oh man doc, she called me a pussy and started saying all sorts of mean things. She even told our mutual friends. I ended up leaving the next morning and never saw her again." "Geez, John that's rough. I'm sorry that happened. And the way she handled it was just atrocious. You know, it's not uncommon for men to occasionally lose an erection. It happens." His eyes opened wide. "However, it can become a persistent problem when sex is imminent, and all the man can think about is 'will I able to perform?'" I explained. "Yes, that's me," he exclaimed. "Have you ever thought about seeing a therapist for this?" I asked. "Hmm? No. I didn't know that was an option. It's kind of embarrassing, you know?" He responded inquisitively. "Look John, I'm sure you don't have anything wrong with your hardware, but maybe you could work on letting go of your ex-girlfriend and the shame you carry around from that experience." He followed up, "What do you mean?" "I mean, your ex-girlfriend gave you a complex and crushed your sexual confidence, and somewhere within you, you believed her words. What if you can find a way to stop identifying with her words?" "I would love that, doc." he said as he sighed. I gave him a referral to a therapist, and he took it.

It's visits like these that are very rewarding. John thought he was stuck with his problem and his only choice was medication. I applauded him for coming in and being open enough to consider looking deeper into his situation. So many men define their "manliness" by their conquests and sexual performance that when they have trouble functioning sexually, they feel that they are less of a "man." Men like John not only have to overcome the socially-engineered concept of "masculinity" but also the judgment about what it means to seek psychotherapy. Being able to ask questions and take the time to think more mindfully is very important for physicians to do with their patients, especially when the problem or concern is likely a psychological one.

In emergency rooms, I've witnessed more mockery of patients with "psych-issues" than I would like to mention. It saddens me.

One can assume, individuals who ridicule people when they are down, are not settled in their own life. For many, it's not uncommon that people in positions of power artificially elevate their sense of self by diminishing others:

I was a third-year resident working in the emergency room on a 12-hour shift. Four of us were in the com-

puter room, where we wrote our provider notes. It was a slow night. A young woman came into the ER with a panic attack and chest pain. She was taken to a room. The nurse came in and exclaimed, "Got another crazy. She's having a panic attack," as she rolled her eyes and threw air quotes. I was so appalled at the arrogance, dismissiveness, and apathy I almost fell out of my chair. No one said a thing. It was as if this type of behavior was accepted. This wasn't the first time I've heard this kind of degradation from hospital employees in many different hospitals around the world, specifically emergency rooms. I was doing my notes on another patient when the same nurse came back in to talk to the patient's doctor, exasperated, she scoffed, "Now she wants Ativan!" The doctor said, "Okay, give her one milligram." The nurse sighed loudly and stomped away to fulfill the order. She returned and told the doctor, "I gave her the medication. She's still complaining. She's crazy!"

"Excuse me!?" I reacted quickly, trying to suppress my anger. I thought, "Oh shit, what have I just started? I guess there's no turning back now." "Excuse me, nurse, but who do you think you are?" I said quite firmly and obviously pissed off. "This woman is in pain and needs your help, and I don't appreciate your behavior!" I was acutely aware that the attending physician and others

were hearing this—ugh. I continued, "It's appalling how you are talking about this patient. I hope you don't room any of my patients tonight!" I walked out of the room, feeling the adrenaline vibrating down to my fingertips.

The more prevalent and normalized *this* type of behavior is among colleagues, the less likely one is to confront it.

Many years have gone by since I stood in the emergency room with that nurse. When I read it back, as a more mature and seasoned doctor, I cringe at my abrasiveness and reactivity. If it happened now, I think it may go something like this:

. . . "I gave her the medication. She's still complaining. She's crazy!" I stand up and walk over to the nurse, "Hi, nurse, what's your name?" "Tammy," she responds. "Hey nurse Tammy, do you have a second? I wanted to talk to you about a patient we have in common. Let's go over here." "Sure Dr. Lewis, but I have to give this woman her medications." "We won't be long. It's okay." We walk over to the next private room where they store supplies. I leave the door open and say, "Thanks Tammy, I pulled you away because I didn't want to say anything in front of the others." "HmHmm," she

replied. I continue, "I couldn't help but notice how you were talking about the patient who is having a panic attack." "What about it?" as she crossed her arms. I said, "Well, to be honest, I think that was a little harsh, you know? I know things can be hectic and maybe you're feeling a lot of pressure? I totally get it, I've been there, trust me." "Yeah," she said as she looked down and closed her eyes in disappointment, and continued, "It's very busy and I'm pulled in 5 different directions and this patient keeps calling me over because she's scared. I have so many things to do and now you're pulling me away." "Tammy, wow, you have a lot on your plate for sure and your job isn't easy. It's enough to make anyone's head spin. Honestly, I don't know how you do it and I really appreciate your hard work." I continue, "But look, Tammy, that lady is in pain, maybe not physical, but it's real. See if you can show her some compassion. If she was okay, she would be at home. She's suffering, you know?" She says softly, "I do, and I will." With a gentle look, "Tammy, thanks for speaking with me and taking time out of your busy night. I'll keep this between us. Hang in there." As she walked out, she raises her hand, "Thanks, doc."

PART
SIX

WHY DOCTORS BURN OUT

BURN, BABY, BURN

"They burned the bridge and ask why I didn't visit."

— Unknown

MARCH 30 IS A SPECIAL DAY, National Doctors' Day. The first Doctors' Day observance was on May 9th, 1933, in Winder, Georgia. The date chosen was the anniversary of the first use of general anesthesia (ether) to surgically remove a neck tumor. However, it wasn't until 1990, that President Bush designated Doctors' Day a national holiday, celebrated on March 30.[19]

It holds the distinction of being shared with National Pencil Day and flanked by National Lemon Chiffon Cake Day and National Crayon Day, just saying.

Medicine is an honorable career filled with experiences that very few will ever get to see or know. Medicine is also challenging. There is immense pressure to perform at the highest level, 100% of the time. There is little room for error when it comes to human lives. Significant, well-researched predictors of burnout exist:

High workloads, clerical burdens, lack of support from colleagues and leaders, diminished feeling of autonomy/control and lack of meaning at work.[20] As one can imagine, certain fields of medicine have higher rates of burnout: *Emergency medicine, Urology, Physical medicine and rehabilitation, and Family Practice.* In 2021, Family Practice was ranked fourth in specialties likely to burn out. Why? It's predictable that the frontline of medicine experiences the most stress. Many factors influence burnout of the physician and may include:

- Lack of control of schedule and free time
- Frequency of being on "call"
- Bureaucracy
- Micromanagement
- Poor self-care / work-life balance
- Chaotic environment
- Personality type
- Debt burden
- Long hours
- Poor reimbursement
- Underappreciated
- The public
- Healthcare reform
- Disenchantment

- Patient volume and so little time
- Paperwork
- Unlimited tasks
- Litigation
- Poorly designed Electronic Medical Records
- Compassion fatigue

Doctors are 15 times more likely to burn out than professionals in any other line of work, and 45% of primary care physicians (PCPs) report that they would quit if they could afford to do so. Physicians have a 10 to 20% higher divorce rate than the general population and, sadly, there are 300 to 400 physician suicide deaths each year.[21]

These are scary statistics, and if I wasn't a doctor, I might not believe them. Companies want physicians to think that offering classes to their employees about "work-life balance" will somehow make up for a system-wide primary care physician burnout epidemic in healthcare.

The system rakes physicians over the burning coals until we become nothing more than embers and ash.

Front-line primary care physicians are acutely aware of the responsibility we have quarterbacking our patients' medical journey hoping we are making the right call each step of the way.

PCPs must have a wealth of information at their fingertips, as we never know what issue will be presented in the clinics. We must know how to handle a smorgasbord of medical concerns from tuberculosis, gout, gynecological health, domestic abuse, joint injections, wound care, anxiety, insomnia, abdominal pain, chest pain, and so on. If that's not enough, most people come in with at least two presenting complaints to deal with during a seven-to eight-minute encounter. I've actually been given a college-ruled, single-spaced piece of paper with 36 complaints written and expected to take care of all of them in one visit. Setting up expectations with our patient is necessary to avoid disappointment, anger, or frustration.

Working for a corporation is one thing, but owning and running your own practice is an entirely different beast altogether. Physicians went to medical school to be doctors and care for the ill, not to be businessmen and businesswomen—except for the few doctorpreneurs. We weren't taught how to run a business, deal with the never-ending clerical work, prepare for surprise audits, insurance companies' claims, or all the bureaucracy at the heart of larger medical organizations. We were taught to care for patients, yet unknowingly are expected to know how to tend to these other areas effectively or risk losing our license, job, or reputation. But no pressure, right? Sometimes I felt that caring for my patients *and* becoming proficient with these other tasks seemed impossible—for many it is. One could be Marcus Welby, M.D. (A fictional general practitioner who tried to treat people as individuals in an age of specialized medicine and uncaring doctors) and still not get it done.

Doctors with great intentions may be spread too thin to do the good work our patients deserve.

What ailed me couldn't be fixed with a vacation. It was time for action. Many variables would be affected if I left the HMO, including job and financial security. Fear and uncertainty plagued me, pushing me to seek counsel and decide my next moves.

Dr. Linzer, Director of the Division of General Internal Medicine at Hennepin County Medical Center in Minneapolis, has studied physician burnout since 1996. He so elegantly stated, "As physicians, we want to be altruistic, but one of the keys to altruism is self-care."

The Physicians' Foundation is an independent group interested in empowering physicians and improving healthcare. Biennially they run a study looking at physician satisfaction and morale, as well as other variables. In 2016 they conducted a survey that was completed by 17,236 physicians—the answers were quite validating.[22] The following tables were adapted from the study:

Which best describes your professional morale and your feelings about the current state of the medical profession?

	2016	2014	2012
Very positive/ optimistic	8.6%	8.8%	3.9%
Somewhat positive/ optimistic	37.5%	35.6%	27.9%
Somewhat negative/ pessimistic	36.0%	37.1%	44.8%
Very negative/ pessimistic	17.9%	18.5%	23.4%

Which best describes how you feel about the future of the medical profession?

	2016	2014	2012
Very positive/ optimistic	6.8%	10.2%	3.1%
Somewhat positive/ optimistic	30.4%	38.7%	19.5%
Somewhat negative/ pessimistic	41.4%	39.5%	45.9%
Very negative/ pessimistic	21.4%	11.6%	31.5%

Which best describes the time you are able to spend with patients?

	2016
My time with patients is always limited	15.6%
My time with patients is often limited	32.9%
My time with patients is sometimes limited	37.6%
I generally have all the time I need to provide the highest standards of care	13.9%

What two factors do you find least satisfying about medical practice?

Long hours/lack of personal time	24.9%
Liability/defensive medicine pressure	40.3%
Reimbursement issues	27.3%
LAck of clinical autonomy	9.2%
Dealing with Medicare.Medicaid/Government regulations	27.4%
Pressure of running a practice	5.6%
Non-clinical paperwork	18.1%
Uncertainty/changes of health reform	21.5%
Managed care	7.6%
EMR Implementation	9.2%
Other	5.1%

*Same group from 2012 study

What TWO factors do you find MOST satisfying about medical practice?

	2016	2014	2012	2008*
Patient relationships	73.8%	78.6%	80.2%	78.17%
Intellectual stimulation	58.7%	65.3%	69.7%	81.69%
Interaction with colleagues	19.7%	22.0%	19.2%	56.18%
Social/ community impact	19.2%	N/A	N/A	N/A
Financial rewards	16.1%	15.2%	11.7%	22.60%
Prestige of medicine	10.2%	12.2%	10.0%	34.86%

*Question asked as: "What do you find most satisfying about medical practice?"

Which of the following best describes your current practice

	2016	2014	2012
I am overextended and overworked	28.2%	31.2%	22.7%
I am at full capacity	52.4%	49.8%	52.8%
I have time to see more patients and assume more duties	19.4%	18.9%	24.6%

To what extent do you have feelings of professional burnout in your medical career?

	2016	2014	2012
No such feelings	10.7%	N/A	N/A
Rarely have these feelings	15.3%	N/A	N/A
Sometimes have these feelings	25.4%	N/A	N/A
Often have these feelings	31.4%	N/A	N/A
Always have these feelings (significant burnout)	17.2%	N/A	N/A

With over one-third of providers having a *negative professional morale*, 41% having a *somewhat negative/pessimistic* view of their profession and one-third feeling *overextended and overworked.* It's no wonder we are losing PCPs in droves.

While 74% of physicians *sometimes* to *always* have feelings of burnout, three out of four physicians still find that patient *relationships* are the most satisfying about their professions (73.8%). The sad part is burnout *always* wins, and our love for our patients just isn't enough to douse those flames.

So now what?

C.Y.A.

"I didn't invent the rainy day, man, I just own the best umbrella."

— Dennis Hope, *Almost Famous*

LITIGATION, DEPOSITIONS, LAWSUITS, supra-condylar fractures, D-Dimers, and suicidal ideation are just some of the issues that cause excessive worry for a physician, especially in private practice. For the most part, physicians work defensively to avoid legal pitfalls, while still trying to balance compassion and evidenced based medicine. There are certainly instances where physicians should be held accountable, such as: Injury caused by a wrongly dispensed medication, surgical equipment left in the abdominal cavity of patients, wrong leg amputation, gross misconduct or when the wrong blood type is given, etc. Fear of litigation is a black cloud that follows us everywhere, especially its potential effects on our livelihood and reputation. Physicians are prone to errors like anyone else and given the potential impact on our patients, the stakes are high to avoid mistakes. When you mix in high patient volume, rushed medical visits, never-ending tasks, fatigue, and fear of being sued, the risk of errors increases dramatically.

OB-GYNs and surgeons are among the top specialties being sued, as cited in a 2015 *Medscape* study. This would account for the $100,000 or more per year malpractice policies for these specialties. *Medscape* surveyed nearly 4,000 primary care physicians and selected specialists to find out if and why they were sued, how the lawsuit affected their career and patient care decisions, and what these doctors suggested to reduce the number of lawsuits. The report shows the long-term effects, both emotional and financial, of malpractice suits on vulnerable doctors.[23]

Further statistics show that 60% of physicians over 55 years old will have been named or been in a lawsuit themselves. One respondent in the *Medscape* survey wrote, "The older you get, the more you have to lose." Interestingly, men were more likely to be sued than women. Forty-two percent of respondents felt that large organizations aren't doing enough to prevent lawsuits.

Marc Siegel, MD, an internist, author and professor of medicine at New York University Langone Medical Center, and a senior *Fox News* medical contributor, mentioned that "Courts are unpredictable, and the stress of being sued—with years of depositions, worry, and damage to your reputation—is a devastating experience, even if there's no payment to the patient (M. 2015)."[24]

Not only does *fear* of litigation burden the physician, but when the physician does go to trial, a vast majority of them will spend more than 40 hours on preparation and meetings, prior to going to court. This process takes the physicians away from their office hours and patient care, which means patients get less access and physicians get less reimbursement. Private practice physicians will take the biggest hit because, as opposed to larger organizations that pay salaries, offer time off for court and pay for legal representation, traditional private practices don't make money unless they *see* patients.

I have been named in a few lawsuits where I *wasn't* the defendant but happened to be the plaintiff's primary care physician. It's an awful feeling when lawyers, who have no medical expertise, try to make the physician (me) feel incompetent:

I was sitting across from three lawyers, a video camera, a court reporter and our organization's legal counsel, nervously awaiting the start of my first deposition. The plaintiff was a young 20s female who was using a piece of exercise equipment that malfunctioned and rebounded into her forehead, causing a depressed skull fracture. She now suffers from migraines, headaches and anxiety. The defendants were the legal team that represented the store and the manufacturer of the equipment. Since I was her primary care physician, the defendants wanted to see if the patient had any of her current symptoms prior to the injury. All I could think about was my counsel stating, "Just keep your answers short. Yes and no will do. Don't say too much."

The deposition started and immediately the friendly smiles of the defendant's council flattened into perfectly horizontal slits. "Oh, shit," I thought. They asked me a slew of generic questions for the first 45 minutes, while they occasionally smiled with a "You're full of shit, doc" look. Maybe I was projecting.

They asked, "Do you remember this patient ever having anxiety?" I responded, "I don't recall." "Doctor Lewis, please refer to page 79 in the folder in front of you. Is this your note? "Yes," I said. "Please read the first part of your note for us, please." I began, "This is a 24-year-old female coming in because she hasn't been sleeping well. She has been under a lot of stress and complains of some anxiety related to work, likely keeping her up. She has trouble both falling and staying asleep. She has no other complaints. No feelings of depression." "What did you do?" asked the lawyer. "I recommended a Benadryl to try and help her sleep, as well as offered some techniques to help at bedtime." I wiped my brow. Upon seeing the next sentence, I realized what they were trying to do, "and if it continued to possibly talk to a therapist who could help with her work stresses and associated anxiety," "So you thought she was anxious?" they asked. "Not exactly," I said. In a snarky tone he asked, "Well, you wrote it. Does that mean your note is wrong?" I answered, "My note isn't wrong. And I didn't say she had anxiety in the common sense of the word; she was having a reaction to normal life circumstances." They said, "But you said she had anxiety, so should I believe you didn't know what you were talking about?" "I object!" said the plaintiff's lawyer, "Where are you going with this?" The questioning lawyer said, "I'm trying to establish that she had a history of anxiety before her injury." (The judge would decide later if the next line of questioning would be admissible because this was a taped deposition).

I crossed my hands in front of me. I looked across the table, feeling a bit nervous and said, "The way I am feeling right now is a little anxiety-provoking, but I'm not anxious," making air quotes. I continued, "Just like a situation where someone got stuck in an elevator and didn't like enclosed places. Their central nervous system would likely go into fight or flight creating the experience of anxiety. Does this mean you have anxiety? No. It means you had a reaction to an uncomfortable situation." They chuckled, and I gulped. We moved on.

After some time, the lawyers went down another path, trying to establish that her headaches were present before the injury, "Dr. Lewis, if you would please turn to page 145 in the folder and read your note." As I was reading, I thought, "Hmm, why this note? She only needed a work note for her boss from an illness she had last week." "Dr. Lewis," the lawyer asked, "I see that you gave the patient 600 milligrams of ibuprofen." "Yes," I replied. "Why did you give it to her?" he asked. I looked through my note and didn't see the reason why and responded, "Not sure, sir." "Was she in pain?" "It doesn't look like it at that point, according to my note," I said, confused. He continues, "Well, do you always give ibuprofen when someone needs a work note?" I said, "Seriously? No." "Then why would you give this to her?" he responded. "Not sure, I don't recall . . .and I didn't write why in my note, but there are plenty of reasons why one would receive this, and it's not that uncommon to fill a medication like this if a patient comes in and asks for a refill."

I sat back in my chair, suddenly aware of all the people there staring at me, including the video camera. "Would headaches be one of those reasons?" With a

*furrowed brow, "Sure, as well as menstrual cramps."
"Thank you. Dr. Lewis, but this could've been for headaches, correct?" "Yes, I suppose," I said, frustrated. At
this point, I was getting irritated because they were
trying to prove incompetence or that my patient was
lying. It's quite the skill, to be honest. "Can you tell me
other times you gave this to her?" "Umm, I would have
to look through the chart." I said. "Let's take a 15-
minute break and let Dr. Lewis look through the chart,"
one of the lawyers said.*

*As I searched through the chart, I found a piece of
information they must have missed. Eighty pages back,
my note showed that I gave this medication for a
sprained ankle. As the break ended, the lawyer continued, "So, Dr. Lewis, did you find anything?" "Yes," I
said in a dry tone, "on page 54, it shows that the
ibuprofen was initially given for a sprained ankle, not
headaches." I stood up at this point, dropped the mic,
and walked out. Not really. They seemed surprised
because they didn't know that was in the note. They
huddled quickly and whispered unintelligibly for a
moment. Our counsel said, "Okay, can we move on
now?" We moved on. Two and a half hours later, we
finished.*

If the initial reason for the ibuprofen was not in the chart, there would have been no proof that the medicine wasn't for migraines, thus could've hurt this part of the case. Every word we write in our medical records is at risk of being scrutinized during litigation or deposition and, therefore, can and will be used against us in a court of law. In medicine, it is said, if it isn't written, it didn't happen. When writing our notes, it's imperative for providers to keep in mind, "If I was on trial, is my note defensible?"

WOULD YOU LIKE FRIES WITH THAT?

"She works hard for the money.
So hard for it, honey.
She works hard for the money
So you better treat her right."

— Donna Summer, "She Works Hard for the Money"

MOST DOCTORS FINISH MEDICAL SCHOOL with around $250,000-$350,000 in student loan debt. Primary care physicians make the third lowest salary in medicine, with pediatricians making up the bottom. When it comes to a family practice resident's (post-graduate training) salary, we make just over minimum wage.

Despite the Accreditation Council for Graduate Medical Education (ACGME) supposedly limiting duty work hours for residents to an *average* of 80 hours per week, many first- and second-year residents log 100-130 hours. The key phrase here is an *average of 80 hours,* which means in a four-week month, a resident can work 110 hours on week one, 80 hours on week two, 60 hours on week three, and 70 hours on week four. This averages out to 80 hours per week. If we were to calculate the hourly salary of resident physicians during the three to five years of training, with an average salary of $51,000 per year, that equates to about $13.00 per hour, while fast food service employees are demanding $15.00 per hour. Hmm? To add insult to injury, doctors are expected to start the payback process of their $250,000+ student loans, which isn't doable, so they defer or go into hardship forbearance while the interest accrues. By the time residency is over, the student loan debt may be upwards of $350,000!

I was a first-year resident on my surgical rotation and was about to find my on-call schedule for the next week. I walked over to the schedule and found my name. I was taken aback as I saw my name on Monday, Wednesday and Friday for on-call duty. I shook my head and said, "What the fuck?!" I asked the chief, "Is this right?" As I grimaced, "Am I really on Q2?" "Yup!" he exclaimed. I was deflated, knowing what kind of week that would be.

Q2 means on-call every two days—cue the dread. A

surgical on-call day went like this: I would show up at the hospital and meet with my surgical team promptly at 5:45 a.m. to discuss cases and what occurred the night prior. Then we would round on the patients (as a team, go from patient to patient on our list, check in, have discussions, etc.). Throughout the day, I would continue rounding, doing tasks, admitting patients, and occasionally assisting surgeries until about 4-5:00 p.m. At this point, all the other team members would go home, and my senior resident and I would take over the surgical team admitting new patients and tending to patients on the floor until the morning. There were times we didn't sleep all night. As the sun rose, I would grab another cup of coffee and head back to the meeting room where everyone would gather. It's 5:45 a.m. again. We would present the overnight admissions and disperse the rounding schedules. It was déjà vu. It's the 25th hour. We would finish rounding around 9:00 a.m., attend meetings until noon before I could go home around 1:00 p.m. and do it again the next day (and two days after). It was rough.

California is ranked 47 out of 50 in a 2016 cost of living (COL) study, while Mississippi is ranked #1 with the (lowest COL).[25] The atrocity here is that California physicians make less money than the states with the lowest COL. With the average home prices in California being $626,000 (for a small two-bedroom) and home rentals soaring, many physicians moonlight to make extra money just to pay the $84,000 yearly nut ($3,000 rent or mortgage plus $4,000 student loan repayment every month-approximated). It's a lot of internal overhead. Only about 50% of physicians in family practice feel they are fairly compensated. At the same time, approximately the same number are satisfied with their career.

Interestingly, only 4% of physicians are in *concierge medicine/direct primary care (DPC)*, yet this group is most satisfied with their career.

The basis of any traditional model of medicine is the ICD (*International Classification of Disease*), now in its 10th edition. Here are a few examples of commonly used diagnostic codes:

Hypertension: I-10
Diabetes type II without complications: E11.9
Major Depressive Disorder, recurrent, unspecified: F33.9
Adjustment reaction: F43.0

These are only four of the 155,000 codes that the ICD has created.

The numbers after the decimal help improve the accuracy of the diagnosis. These figures can extend up to four characters after the decimal point, with every character increasing the complexity of the diagnoses. Reimbursements have become increasingly complicated given the likelihood of human error when navigating the labyrinth of coding. The more detailed, difficult, and convoluted these codes are the more likely one is to make an error; a *positive* for insurance companies given that they can deny payment to the provider.

Given the fact that reimbursements are critical to the providers solvency, many need to hire a coding specialist to oversee their providers—increasing the providers' overhead.

With the increased complexity of billing, denial of payment is a likely outcome, leading the physician to see more patients to make up for this decrease in revenue.

To add insult to injury, Medicare released its Physician Fee Schedule (PFS) in 2021, which showed drastic cuts in payments across all specialties. These cuts represent the lowest reimbursements in the last 25 years.[26] All of this was on the heels of the Covid-19 pandemic, which devastated large and small businesses alike (including medical practices). If Medicare payments can't keep up with inflation, how are physicians supposed to continue delivering quality healthcare?

Can someone call Doc Brown and Marty McFly and let them know Medicare is reimbursing at 1996 rates! Please send a DeLorean.

PART SEVEN

THE CREATION OF
PATHOLOGY

THE DSM AND HOMOSEXUALITY

"'I am concussed,' I announced, entirely sure of my self-diagnosis."

— John Green

THE DIAGNOSTIC AND STATISTICAL MANUAL *of Mental Disorders* (DSM) is the standard reference guide for clinicians and mental health practitioners when needing to make a proper diagnosis. Interestingly, pre-World War II, the first edition of the DSM was released to classify mental health disorders but was mainly put in place to gather statistical mental health information on people in the United States. After WWII, the DSM underwent many changes in an attempt to mainstream its use in patient care[27].

In 1973 many changes were controversial, mainly the diagnosis related to *homosexuality*:

In 1973 homosexuality per se was removed from the DSM-II classification of mental disorders and replaced by the category Sexual Orientation Disturbance. This represented a compromise between the view that preferential homosexuality is invariably a mental disorder and the view that it is merely a normal sexual variant. While the 1973 DSM-II controversy was highly public, more recently a related but less public controversy involved what became the DSM-III category of Ego-dystonic Homosexuality...

This means that prior to 1973, homosexuality was regarded as a mental disorder. So, in 1973, when the medical establishment changed the term to *Sexual Orientation Disturbance,* many still held on to the *belief* that homosexuality was *preferential* and classified as a mental disorder.

In 1968, The DSM-II categorized homosexuality into the following classification:

302 Sexual deviations:
This category is for individuals whose sexual interests are directed primarily toward objects other than people of the opposite sex, toward sexual acts not usually associated with coitus, or toward coitus performed under bizarre circumstances as in necrophilia, pedo-

philia, sexual sadism, and fetishism. Even though many find their practices distasteful, they remain unable to substitute normal sexual behavior for them. This diagnosis is not appropriate for individuals who perform deviant sexual acts because normal sexual objects are not available to them.

- 302.0 Homosexuality
- 302.1 Fetishism
- 302.2 Pedophilia
- 302.3 Transvestitism
- 302.4 Exhibitionism
- 302.5 Voyeurism
- 302.6 Sadism
- 302.7 Masochism
- 302.8 Other sexual deviation
- 302.9 Unspecified sexual deviation

If you think that's bad, read what DSM-I had to say 21 years prior, in 1952:

OOQ-x63 Sexual deviation
This diagnosis is reserved for deviant sexuality, which is not symptomatic of more extensive syndromes, such as schizophrenic and obsessional reactions. The term includes most cases formerly classed as "psychopathic personality with pathologic sexuality." The diagnosis will specify the type of the pathologic behavior, such as

homosexuality, transvestism, pedophilia, fetishism and sexual sadism (including rape, sexual assault, mutilation).

In 1975, the DSM-III (third edition) was released and was revolutionary in its content by beginning to classify diagnoses via a multi-axial system (an evaluation in terms of several different domains of information), as psychiatry and psychology use now.

One must be grateful to our predecessors that challenged the status-quo of their time, allowing for meaningful change in de-pathologizing sexual orientation.

THE SCARLET LETTER

"I am what I am."

— Popeye

PROVIDERS SHOULD NOT UNDERESTIMATE THE power of a proper diagnosis. Each new label given to our patients may have significant effects on the patient's future, especially when the diagnosis is made hastily, inaccurately, or both. Our patients trust that we will always do what's best for them no matter how busy we are—time restraints are no excuse for a hasty diagnosis.

I understand when the pressure is on, and the provider is sitting in their office after the visit writing their note, sometimes it's arduous to find the most accurate diagnostic code to match the patient's issue. You're already 30 minutes behind, and two patients are waiting. You haven't eaten lunch. The phone rings, and the computer chimes notifying you that another patient message just arrived. So, you say, "Screw it! I can't find it, so I'll just choose this one, <click> close enough," not realizing how this code can affect the patient's future life and health insurance premiums. Or worse yet, how this diagnosis may impact them when they receive their after-visit summary and see a diagnosis never discussed with them.

These labels seem benign on the surface but can have a significant impact on our patients:

Eleanor was a 52-year-old female whom I saw twice very early in my career for issues relating to her kidneys. I diagnosed her with CKD-III (chronic kidney disease stage III) due to readings on her most recent labs. In retrospect, a more accurate diagnosis would have been acute renal insufficiency because she was dehydrated. Her prior labs were normal. Months went by, and she returned to the office. "Hey, Dr. Mike. I wanted to talk with you about this diagnosis," as she points to her past after-visit summary. "Sure!" I said. "I went to apply for life insurance, and they wouldn't insure me. They said I had kidney damage. I freaked out. Do I need dialysis? I've never heard this before," she said, concerned. I thought that's strange. "Okay, let me check your chart," as I searched the medical record. There it was—the diagnosis of CKD-III that I entered during our last visit. I looked at her other labs and they were okay. The latest ones she did last week were perfect. "I apologize Eleanor. Last time I saw you, your kidneys were a bit sluggish from the dehydration. I didn't put the correct diagnosis. And to be honest, I didn't know it would affect your life insurance. I'm so sorry." Politely but irritated, she said, "That's okay." I removed the diagnosis and left a note in the computer explaining why the diagnosis was removed. At the end of our visit, I wrote a letter that she could provide to her insurance company. Eleanor never returned to see me again. Can you blame her?

I made a clerical mistake, which led to a negative outcome. Not only that, but I also caused her fear and anxiety, which I'm sure she greatly underplayed during our visit—She thought she needed dialysis! Can you imagine what she must have been thinking? I felt horrible. But how was I supposed to know about the insurance issue? No one ever taught us that. There's no continuing education on it. It's not in the books. There's no training for this. But that's no excuse! If I made the most accurate diagnosis initially, we could've avoided this issue altogether.

Classically, psychiatry is known for its liberal use of medications. Though, many people see them as patient mills and drug dispensaries, they remain invaluable to the medical field. Just like primary care providers, they are under similar time restraints, thus root-cause therapy doesn't often occur on *the couch*. The chronic medicating of patients, other than the chemically-imbalanced and severely mentally ill, can strip away a patient's opportunity for emotional growth:

Ken was a 47-year-old male with complaints of excessive worry and anxiety. He came to my office to see if he could get some help. Unfortunately, I was out of the office and another provider saw him. The provider told me, "I saw your patient Ken yesterday. He was anxious, so I sent him off to psych and gave him some Xanax." "I see," I said with a straight face in a monotone voice, "Thank you for seeing him."

About a month later, Ken came in for a follow-up. "Hey, Doctor Mike!" "Hey Ken, glad to see you. Are we following up on your last visit?" I asked. Ken responded, "Yeah, I went to see the psychiatrist." "And?" I asked. "He gave me all sorts of medicine. He told me I was depressed and anxious and thought I may have ADD, so he gave me Lexapro, Xanax, Ambien to help me sleep AND a prescription for Adderall," as he held his bag of pills in front of me and jiggled it like it was a maraca. "Whoa!" I exclaimed, "How do you feel now?" "I feel better, I was going through a bit of a rough time," he said, "but I didn't take any of the medicines." "Oh?"

I replied. "I don't understand, Doctor Mike, I was there for like 15 minutes, and he gave me all these meds. He didn't even know me! Aren't these dangerous or addictive?" "They can be," I said as I scratched my head, "but I'm glad you didn't take them. You know it's not abnormal for many psychiatrists to give meds like these without inquiring deeper into your life's current situation. Did he recommend a therapist?" "No, he said just come back in a month," I put my head into my hand and said, "Ken, why don't you come back and see me in a month instead." I placed my hand on his shoulder, "Do you have any questions?" He said, "No doc, I'm good." I shook his hand and left the room, "See you later, buddy."

In this case, I was relieved to learn that Ken was autonomous in his decision-making. It's situations like this that become dangerous for patients and inhibits their natural ability to move through difficult situations. Let alone, can leave a stain on their medical record. I understand that as a physician, we are taught to relieve all suffering. We are taught to make patients feel better and try to end or minimize pain (psychological or physical). I don't believe that *all* suffering needs to be treated with medication, which begs the question, "Is there a benefit to suffering?" To quote Khalil Gibran:

*"Out of suffering have emerged the strongest souls; the
most massive characters are seared with scars."*

While, I wasn't in the room with him during his
short visit, I know one thing, prescribing that many
psychotropics was inappropriate.

The data regarding psychiatric medications is eye-
opening. In a study by BMC on "Trends in GP (general
practitioners) prescribing of psychotropic medications
among young patients aged 16–24 years,"[28] 9,112 out of a
total of 77,466 young patients were identified as having a
mental health condition. 11,934 psychotropic prescriptions were provided to 3967 (43.5%) of them over the
study period. Antidepressants accounted for 81.4% of
total psychotropic prescriptions, followed by anxiolytics
(9.6%). Yes, 43% of young patients between 16-24 were
given psychotropics by primary care physicians! It's
alarming, to say the least.

Steven Hollon, Ph.D., is a psychology professor at
Vanderbilt University who has conducted extensive
research on the effectiveness of antidepressants. He says,
"I would say at least half the folks being treated with
antidepressants aren't benefiting from the active
pharmacological effects of the drugs themselves, but a
placebo effect." He concludes, "If people knew more, I
think they would be a little less likely to go down the

medication path than the psychosocial treatment path."

Many medications for depression and anxiety are helpful, but can also be quite dangerous, addictive or have serious/significant side effects.

Medications such as SSRIs can lead to significant weight gain and anorgasmia (inability to reach orgasm). In contrast, medications for anxiety can be so addictive that if taken off them abruptly, they can cause seizures. Sadly, these pills are some of the most prescribed in primary care medicine, with alprazolam (Xanax) being the most prescribed psychiatric medication.

Certainly, some patients have a chemical imbalance that needs to be adjusted by medications via psychiatry. Expertise in pharmacology, attention to our patients' relationship to their diagnoses and medications is just as important.

Awareness of not just the biochemical aspect of the patient but the person standing in front of you is also highly important—we never know how our patients will react once they receive their new diagnosis. Some diagnoses hold more stigma or emotional charge than others.

SQUARE PEG...

"If it doesn't fit... You must acquit."

— *Johnnie Cochran*

INSURANCE COMPANIES ARE HEDGING THEIR BETS that more revenue is made from premiums than the money needed to pay out for illnesses. As discussed, these companies require diagnoses for every medical visit submitted as a claim so that they can reimburse the provider or medical corporation appropriately.

As I mentioned earlier, providers don't give much thought to how the choice of diagnosis may affect the patients' future. I know I didn't for many years. When patients receive *any* new diagnosis it's important that it's accurate. For example, the differences in pre-diabetes and diabetes or acute renal insufficiency and chronic kidney disease stage III, or adjustment disorder and depression, can have dramatic effects in multiple areas of a patient's life, like Eleanor's.

Life insurance interviews involve many questions

about one's personal health history to determine risk (of death). One of which, *"Have you seen a psychiatrist, psychologist or other therapist in the last 10 years?"* If the client says, "yes," it's possible that it may affect their premiums. But what if the client was grieving? What if the client wanted to better themselves? What if the client was in a relationship crisis?

To illustrate this, below is the diagnostic criteria for major depressive disorder:

- Depressed mood or a loss of interest or pleasure in daily activities for more than two weeks.
- Mood represents a change from the person's baseline.
- Impaired function: social, occupational, educational.
- Specific symptoms, at least 5 of these 9, present nearly every day:
  (1) Depressed mood or irritable most of the day, nearly every day, as
    (a) indicated by either subjective report (e.g., feels sad or empty) or observation made
    (b) by others (e.g., appears tearful).
  (2) Decreased interest or pleasure in most activities, most of each day
  (3) Significant weight change (5%) or change in appetite
  (4) Change in sleep: Insomnia or hypersomnia

(5) Change in activity: Psychomotor agitation or retardation

(6) Fatigue or loss of energy

(7) Guilt/worthlessness: Feelings of worthlessness or excessive or inappropriate guilt

(8) Concentration: diminished ability to think or concentrate, or more indecisiveness

(9) Suicidality: Thoughts of death or suicide, or has suicide plan

At any given time, most medical students and residents would meet the criteria for depression using the criteria above. Many of them working 30-hour, sleep-deprived shifts. This high stress, physically demanding, emotionally draining work, can take its toll. Lack of sleep leads to *fatigue*, which can affect *concentration* and influence *mood*. One can imagine that this constellation of symptoms would lead to anhedonia (*decreased interest or pleasure in most enjoyable activities*). Given the fact that most residencies last more than *two weeks*, they meet the threshold for major depression. This illustrates how important it is to factor in the context of the patient's presenting issue with their life situation, before making a diagnosis.

Insurance companies and organizations encourage standardized questionnaires to streamline the diagnosis of certain conditions, particularly depression, ADD, and anxiety: Patient Health Questionnaire #9 (PHQ-9) and the Beck's Depression Inventory (BDI). These are screening tools given to patients during a visit and scored by the clinician to get a rough estimate of someone's mood state. These pint-sized diagnostic tools may work as a starting-off point for deeper dialogue. Often when someone scores in the "you may be depressed" zone, the knee jerk-reaction is to send them to "psych" (psychiatry).

What if, instead of interpreting these diagnostic tools as conclusive, we encourage a dialogue with our patients? The patient may not have been aware that the symptoms that they indicated on the questionnaire(s) warrant further discussion.

In fact, this may be the only opportunity the patient has to explore their symptoms with a professional. We must capitalize on this opportunity.

When I worked for the HMO, physicians were encouraged to use these tools and make a diagnosis fit. The Centers for Medicare and Medicaid Services (CMS) would increase reimbursement or reward them accordingly for certain diagnoses. There are ethical considerations when a patient's diagnosis is coerced by bureaucratic entities via financial reward.

Corporations or medical providers that accept

Medicare or Medicaid are frequently audited by the Feds (CMS). This oversight ensures organizations conform to specific electronic medical records (EMR) standards *(Meaningful Use)* and to make sure they are coding correctly (*CMS 5-Star* ranking).

To add to the coding confusion, CMS created HCC codes (Hierarchal Condition Categories). The HCC is a risk-adjustment model initially designed to estimate future health costs. More than 9,700 ICD-10 diagnosis codes map to CMS's 86 HCC codes.

For example, someone with diabetes would have a specific risk based on their HCC coding. But, if this person with diabetes takes insulin *and* has heart failure, they would have a higher HCC risk associated, which increases reimbursement for the corporation or provider.

This is appropriate given that most patients with higher risk will require more visits. If I were still treating Medicare patients, I would want appropriate reimbursement to reflect the complexity of my visits too. As long as reimbursements are made without manipulation (upcoding by provider) or coercion (by the corporation), there's no problem.

Many metrics are used to determine physician bonuses in HMOs and other large corporations, including patient satisfaction surveys, number of patients seen and coding. Willful provider upcoding (purposely coding higher than it should be) is illegal and unethical. But seriously, who is going to catch an *adjustment disorder* (no HCC code) "misdiagnosed" as *major depression* (has HCC code)? Or a *history* of *severe asthma* (No HCC) "misdiagnosed" as *COPD (Chronic Obstructive Pulmonary Disease—has HCC)*? Or the person with diabetes (has HCC) who *once* complained of tingling in their hand, "misdiagnosed" as *diabetes with complications (neuropathy—higher HCC)*? Ding, ding, ding. No one would be the wiser! This is one-way upcoding is encouraged.

So, the visit is complete, and the patient receives their after-visit summary, goes home, and freaks out because they have just learned that they have Major depression, COPD, or diabetes with complications. The unintended consequences of upcoding are numerous.

Below are the top five HCC codes,[29] which are easy to get wrong, or manipulate:

1. Diabetes with Chronic Complications (HCC 18)
2. Specified Heart Arrhythmias (HCC 96)
3. Chronic Obstructive Pulmonary Disease (HCC 111)
4. Major Depressive, Bipolar, and Paranoid Disorders (HCC 59)
5. Morbid Obesity (HCC 22)

The focus is revenue *disguised* as better patient care. Shameful. Manipulating a diagnosis and willfully upcoding to be compliant for CMS is not only fraudulent but violates our Hippocratic oath and betrays our patient's trust.

How do we regain our sovereignty as physicians, while we are dependent on the bureaucracy for survival?

I. Don't. Know.

WHERE WAS I THAT DAY?

"And Hansel said to Gretel: Let us drop these breadcrumbs so that together we find our way home. Because losing our way would be the most cruel of things."

— Lucas Scott, *One Tree Hill*

THE WORDS, "WAS I ASLEEP THAT DAY?" echo throughout the sterile, tan hallways of medical clinics all over the United States every summer as doctors enter their first visit codes as new attendings (supervising physician, just out of residency). Most doctors, even seasoned ones, are not intimately familiar with the convoluted process of coding. A residency program rarely prepares the new doctor enough to run and operate a practice, including the basics of coding in large medical corporations. Yet, all physicians need to know this almost as much as they need to know how to treat high blood pressure. Luckily, my residency program prepared us well. We were one of few programs in the country that had a required "practice management" month for third-year residents. In addition, we had multiple training sessions and audits on proper coding throughout our three-year program, so when we were "let loose," most of us were reasonably equipped with the tools to code correctly. In my experience providers have little knowledge of proper coding, and simply . . . just . . . guess.

Other physicians had to learn on the job, taking time away from doing what they were trained to do. Most residents aren't prepared for this after residency. There wasn't even a warning. We were just thrown into the wild and told, "Survive!" So, when chart audits came, most physicians just improvised their coding, and blindly made the corrections that the auditors told us to.

Some EMRs have a point-and-click interface that calculate your coding, which sounds great. Unfortunately, they are clunky, impersonal, time consuming and, get this, code inaccurately. Some are so bad that I swore I would never work from a company that uses this type of EMR software, regardless of salary—it's too much overhead.

Considering the volume of patients and time restraints, physicians must work with increased efficiency, sometimes entering codes that *almost* fit but aren't quite accurate. Increasing accuracy in coding is especially important with mental health diagnoses.

Active listening, asking thoughtful questions and having good reference material can help avoid situations like Eleanor's.

PART EIGHT

COMPASSION TRAINING: WHY IT'S NOT ENOUGH

LUNCH MEETING AT NOON: COMPASSION 101

"If you want others to be happy, practice compassion. If you want to be happy, practice compassion."

— Dalai Lama

WHILE EMPATHY IS THE ABILITY to understand and share the feelings of others, sympathy (pity) doesn't help anyone. So, what is compassion? Compassion is empathy with the added desire to help. It can't be faked. Most people can *feel* inauthenticity—can't you? While compassion training yields good actors, we really should leave that to Meryl Streep. Clinician-focused lunch-and-learn sessions on "Compassion Training for Healthcare Providers" are frequent in major medical corporations:

I arrived at the lunch-and-learn, to see the chairs were moved from the typical front-facing positions to an uncomfortable circle so we all could look at each other as we spoke. I didn't mind it, but I knew others in the room would rather be inconspicuous. We were told by the instructor, "Okay, providers, we are going to work with all of you today on compassion." "Kill me!" I thought, smiling at the irony. "Who can tell me the difference between compassion and empathy?" the instructor asked. A few hands cautiously raised, and many reasonable answers filled the room. The class continued, "Who wants to role play?" As expected, no one raised their hands until the silence was so uncomfortable that this female physician stood up and sat in the middle of the circle.

The instructor said, "Okay, I'm going to be the patient and want you to be the doctor. Please show me how you may interact with this patient." She went into character, "Hi doctor, so many things have been going on recently. I just feel so sad." The doctor asked, "I see, how long have you been feeling this way?" The instructor answered, "Maybe a week or two . . . I just found out I have breast cancer and am feeling so sad about it. I'm not sure what to do." The physician quickly answered, "Oh? "What kind of breast cancer?" Confused, the instructor said, "Breast? What kind? I don't know what kind." "Hmmm," replied the doctor.

There was silence.

Was that my stomach growling? I started counting the carpet fibers . . . I couldn't just stare. I wonder what's for dinner? Giving the doctor the benefit of the doubt, I thought, "Okay, so maybe she has stage fright." The silence continued. Bueller? Bueller? Bueller? Like a bolt of lightning ripped from the sky, she abruptly uttered, "Umm, that's horrible, have you seen an oncologist?" the doctor said in a defeated monotone voice, "Okay, good." I imagined slapping my forehead. The instructor broke character and looked up, "Would anyone have said anything differently? Anyone?" I thought, "besides everything?" A few responses were shouted out. "Okay, thank you," the instructor looked at the doctor, "You can take a seat now."

The class continued with more group and one-to-one role play. I wanted to poke out my eyeballs.

Compassion is an innate human trait, which is nurtured during early childhood development through relationships with primary attachment figures.

While most people can learn new techniques such as active listening, motivational interviewing and reflectively responding, performing these techniques alone falls short when there isn't a solid base to work from.

Regardless of our roles in life, we are all human, and share the burdens of existence. When we remember this, connecting to our patients is effortless.

COMPASSION SIESTA?

"The stress resulting from helping, or wanting to help, a traumatized or suffering person."

— Figley, C. (1995)

OUCH? CAN COMPASSION HURT? Dr Charles Figley, director, Tulane University Traumatology Institute says, "Compassion Fatigue is a state experienced by those helping people or animals in distress; it is an extreme state of tension and preoccupation with the suffering of those being helped to the degree that it can create a secondary traumatic stress for the helper." The website compassionfatigue.org explains,

> *Caring too much can hurt. When caregivers focus on others without practicing self-care, destructive behaviors can surface. Apathy, isolation, bottled-up emotions, and substance abuse head a long list of symptoms associated with the secondary traumatic stress disorder now labeled: Compassion Fatigue. While*

the effects of Compassion Fatigue can cause pain and
suffering, learning to recognize and manage its
symptoms is the first step . . .

Studies show that this phenomenon requires a therapeutic relationship between the healthcare provider and the patient.[30] An individual's capacity for empathy and ability to engage or enter a therapeutic relationship is central to compassion fatigue.

Caring for patients is a complex and stressful job that carries much responsibility. The key to success in avoiding this issue with patients isn't disconnection and apathy. Instead, it's self-care and compassion. Wait, so the cure to compassion fatigue is compassion? I think so, yes! When one is courageous enough to face challenging realities about themselves, the delivery of compassion can become second nature.

But when the provider stops looking inwards, patients can suffer, and the provider's work can take a toll. How can one tolerate a job that demands compassion, and not be compassionate for themselves? Taking care of ourselves is an active process that requires *frequent* check-ins.

Some clinic days are so overwhelmed with grief and sadness that if I didn't have a chance to cry, chill out, or talk about it with my wife (partner, therapist, friend or family member), it would be difficult to recuperate and be present with my patients the next day.

I find it helpful to occupy a space for gratitude and appreciate the moments we get to share with our patients, especially during their most challenging times. Loss of a loved one, end-of-life discussions, new diagnosis of cancer, or simply the fear of a new diagnosis of diabetes, are profound moments in our patients' life.

Due to their selfless nature, empaths are more likely to suffer from compassion fatigue. Some people have gone through their life making everyone else a priority, leaving themselves out of the equation.

The generosity of spirit it takes to be compassionate for another is honorable, yet, if it's not balanced with self-compassion, the empathy may dwindle, leaving us wondering, "Wait, what about me?" The internal process of chronically neglecting ourselves may lead to symptoms of depression or may turn into dopamine-induced, self-defeating behaviors to make us feel worthy: Food. Drugs. Sex. Smoking. Alcohol.

Regardless of the outcome, recall the first lesson when you're a passenger on an airplane:

*If cabin pressure is lost, the panels above your seat will open, and oxygen masks will drop down. If this happens, place the mask over **your** nose and mouth,*

and adjust it as necessary. Be sure to adjust your mask
before *helping others.*

In other words, help yourself first, so you can be available for everyone else.

A survey of 800 recently hospitalized patients and 510 physicians found broad agreement that compassionate care is "very important" to successful medical treatment. However, only 53% of patients and 58% of physicians said that the healthcare system generally provides compassionate care.[31]

Compassion fatigue can also be described as the convergence of secondary traumatic stress (STS) and cumulative burnout (BO), a state of physical and mental exhaustion caused by a depleted ability to cope with one's everyday environment.[32] Offering yet another opportunity for self-examination. This fatigue likely exits because of something we are ignoring within us. It's not just an entity that stands on its own, separate from us. It is because of us that it exists. Of course, no one said being introspective is easy, but our well-being is worth the effort.

When we are not present with ourselves, apathy may creep in, leading to the suffering of both you and your patients.

That's why it's just as important to be as curious

about ourselves as we are about our patient's diseases. Ask the question, why am I having this reaction? Fear of death? Fear of illness? Fear of intimacy? In other words, what is it within us that's perpetuating the issue of compassion fatigue?

Get curious. Get better.

Exercising compassion for *both* you and your patients is foundational in *curing* compassion fatigue.

Do You Have It?

. . . Suffering is necessary until you realize it is unnecessary."

— Eckhart Tolle

DOES EVERYONE HAVE THE ABILITY to be compassionate? Are some people incapable? Compassion lies on a continuum from apathy to empathy. Emmanuel Kant, one of the central figures of philosophy, believed "compassion is, 'mere inclination' and...can negatively interfere with rational acts of reason." Conversely, Darwin's book, *The Expression of Emotions in Man and Animal*s, suggests that compassion and benevolence are an evolved part of human nature, rooted in our brain and biology, and ready to be cultivated for the greater good.

Physiologically, oxytocin, a chemical in our brains produced in the hypothalamus, is partly responsible for feelings of love and compassion. From a baby suckling its mother's bosom to its effects on generosity, it is an essential hormone to understanding the biochemical-basis of compassion.

FREE HUGS

Just ask!
You won't even be charged a copay!

The more oxytocin you release by being affectionate, the more you want to hug, touch, and hold hands. It's a snowball effect that can not only reduce stress hormones but improve meaningful relationships, long-term personal well-being and overall health.

This sign was on the wall of my exam rooms when I worked for an HMO

In a recent study performed by Dacher Keltner, Ph.D., the founding director of the Greater Good Science Center and a professor of psychology, he states:

> *... we have found that when people perform behaviors associated with compassionate love—warm smiles, friendly hand gestures, affirmative forward leans— their bodies produce more oxytocin. This suggests compassion may be self-perpetuating: Being compassionate causes a chemical reaction in the body that motivates us to be even more compassionate.*

I saw a young woman in the urgent care, who shared a recent interaction she had in an emergency room with a provider:

Tina was a 26-year-old female who came to see me for the first time in urgent care because she needed to follow up on a recent ER visit due to abdominal cramping and fear of a miscarriage. "I showed up in the ER with abdominal cramping and nausea. I also found out two weeks ago I was pregnant. The doctor did a bunch of tests, including one for my pregnancy hormone, which they said was low given the timing of my last period. They also did an ultrasound and told me they didn't see anything. They told me my levels were too low and I would have a miscarriage. The doctor was so abrupt and short with me," she said angrily, "she didn't even seem compassionate. It was so matter-of-fact, as if she was telling me, 'Yes, miss, that is a wart on your hand.' She told me to follow up for repeat testing, so here I am." I sat quietly for a moment, soaking it all in. I asked, "Have you been spotting or cramping?" She replied, "No." I said, "I'm sorry you were treated that way. Many providers underestimate the affects a miscarriage can have on a woman. Seemingly some providers forget they are human too." She nodded, "That's exactly how it felt."

I shook my head and continued, "I'm looking at your numbers, and I don't see a problem. I would like to check your labs today and see what happens. The hormone, hCG, doubles every 48 hours in the first trimester of pregnancy. If it doesn't, then there's a high likelihood of miscarriage. I don't want to get your hopes up, but let's just see. I can only imagine that this adds to your stress and worry about this whole thing. I will do your labs, stat."

Three hours later, my medical assistant called me on my cell phone and told me the results had returned for Tina. "Her numbers tripled, Dr. Lewis!" she said excitedly. I thought, "What a F'n relief," and said, "Would you please let her know these results and make an appointment with her OB-GYN asap. She has my phone number so let her know she can call me with any questions." My medical assistant said, "No problem, Dr. Lewis." I sighed with relief. Tina went on to have a full-term, uneventful pregnancy.

What is it that prevents providers from being compassionate in these situations? Their own trauma? Self-protection? Time restraints? Compassion fatigue? Power-trips? A bad day? Whatever the reason, we owe it to the people around us, to be better.

I Know Exactly What You're Going Through

"Platitude: a remark or statement, especially one with a moral content, that has been used too often to be interesting or thoughtful."

— *Oxford English Dictionary*

OFTEN, WE ARE CONFRONTED WITH situations where grief, sadness or fear are present: Maybe a friend says that they're getting divorced, or someone tells you they have a terminal illness, or maybe an acquaintance lost a family member. We are pack animals by nature. Most of us crave connection and companionship during emotionally challenging times. Often, people are at a loss for words for fear of saying the wrong things or being insensitive. It happens to all of us. Understandably, we reach for something, anything to try and soothe the unsoothable. Platitudes, while on the surface seem reasonable and appropriate, fall flat. Think of them as military MREs (meals ready to eat)—just add water, and boom, instant compassion!

Here are a few all-stars:

Just pray.
It's God's will.
You'll get over it
It could be worse.
It was meant to be.
Just think positive.
What's done is done.
It wasn't meant to be.
We all have problems.
Time heals all wounds.
They don't deserve you.
Don't let it get you down.
You're better off without them.
Everything happens for a reason.
Good things come to those who wait.
You have your whole life ahead of you.
Other people go through this every day.
Don't worry, nothing's gonna happen.
If life gives you lemons, make lemonade.
If at first you don't succeed, try, try again.
What doesn't kill you makes you stronger.
Life doesn't give you things you can't handle.

The truth is that upon receiving a platitude, we rarely feel better; sometimes even more alone. What do you think of them? Do they give you a warm gushy feeling inside when you hear them? Are they engaging? Do they encourage intimacy? In most cases, the answer is a resounding "No!" When used alone, platitudes have very little value yet could have significance when used and followed up with deeper penetrating questions and discussion. Phrases like, "What do you have to worry about . . . kids are starving in Africa!" can legitimately lend some perspective (even if in poor taste); however, it's unlikely that this famine-guilt argument helps because the issue still exists, correct?

Each person's suffering is unique. Suffering is suffering.

When our patients are experiencing emotional suffering, there is a natural reflex to want to help. Some suffering can't be alleviated with a prescription or a procedure. In times like these, it's our duty to dig deeper into our black medical bag of tricks and offer up something unique. A safe pace for dialogue, a hug or an empathic ear is all that is needed.

The real skill is letting go of the need to fix the situation or, better yet, addressing our own discomfort in dealing with an unsolvable situation.

It's the quality of connection that truly brings

people closer.

Let's not let the ticking clock and high volume of patients dissuade us from what's important—the patient. We owe them more than a simple, quick reflexive platitude.

When I find myself searching for the *right things to say*, I remember the words of Eckhart Tolle. He would call these platitudes signposts:[33]

> *Don't get stuck on the level of words. A word is no more than a means to an end. It's an abstraction. Not unlike a signpost, it points beyond itself.*

In other words, the answer isn't the platitude itself; it's where it's pointing. So, if we can continue to be curious, ask questions and try not to dismiss our patients, we can point them in the right direction towards healing.

PART
NINE

ABOUT PAIN

THE PAIN MERRY-GO-ROUND?

"We cannot solve our problems with the same thinking we used when we created them."

— Albert Einstein

WHEN YOU THINK OF PAIN, what comes to mind? Physical injury? Mental anguish? Chronic physical pain? Cancer pain? Complex regional pain syndrome? Depression? Drug-seekers? Pain can be physical, psychological or a combination of the two. I wonder, is there a benefit to pain and suffering? I don't think we can separate the two, especially psychosomatic-type pain (pain caused or aggravated by a mental factor such as unresolved trauma, internal conflict, or stress). When discussing the potential *benefits* of pain, I will focus more on the psychological aspect as we move through this section of the book.

When talking about chronic physical pain, the *expectations* of treatment are of the utmost priority.

Often, patients have the unrealistic expectation that pharmaceutical treatment will resolve their pain *completely*, when in fact, it may only reduce it *fractionally*. Emotional pain is a different animal and self-judgment is a primary variable when addressing psychological distress. As a provider, normalizing symptoms and helping people understand that these issues are a normal part of the human experience is critical. It's a vital part in establishing rapport and building a trusting relationship.

A cyclical problem arises when chronic *physical* pain (lasting longer than six months) and *psychological* pain coexist. Physical pain can exacerbate psychological pain, which can disrupt sleep, leading to trouble coping, depression, and worsening pain. Instead of treating the patient experiencing pain with a symptom-focused approach, it's helpful to use (if not already) a holistic approach to provide better care for these patients.

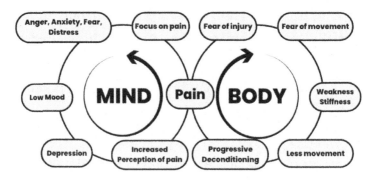

The Mind/Body Pain Cycle

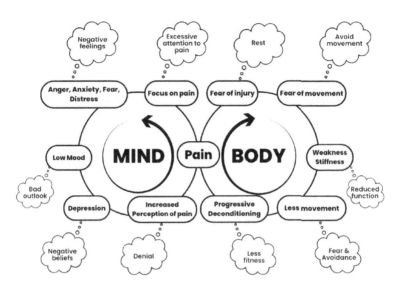

The Mind/Body Pain Cycle: The Internal process

Understanding this cycle[34] can help physicians treat their patients at varying levels of suffering. For example, if we can control the pain enough so patients can sleep through the night, they will be more able to handle daily anxieties and depressive symptoms that usually accompany poorly controlled chronic pain.

In a study looking at more than 45,000 prescriptions, Wayne A. Ray, Ph.D. et al., of the Department of Health Policy, Vanderbilt University School of Medicine, found that long-acting opioids were associated with a 90% increased risk for all-cause mortality—more than fourfold in the first 30 days of treatment.[35] As you can see, pain control treatment can straddle on life and death.

Allowing pain to exist may seem controversial, especially coming from a doctor who believes in minimizing all-cause suffering while observing the tenets of non-malfeasance (first, do no harm). I don't believe *all* pain is beneficial, nor do I think people should *get over it and suck it up.* Hell, I'm not a sadist. Pain is real, whether we are talking about emotional, physical, or psychosomatic pain. Therefore, it's crucial for providers to put aside their bias and listen to their patients and understand the history of the pain before making judgments about it. Treating pain isn't a one-size fits all issue given the subjective nature of it—one person's mild pain is another person's worst pain. Pain tolerance and pain threshold are unique to everyone (these differences can be explained both biochemically and biologically).

Understanding *opioid dependence* is crucial when treating chronic pain. Another complication with the treatment of physical pain is predicting who will respond to which medicine.

In my career, I've learned some valuable lessons when treating pain with OTC pain medicines. Luckily, my patients didn't die, but unfortunately, I've put two people in the hospital after recommending a seemingly benign OTC naproxen for back pain: One I put into acute kidney failure (almost needed urgent dialysis), and the other had an ulcer (that I didn't know about), which bled profusely.

I learned a big lesson to ask everyone about kidney problems and ulcers before starting NSAIDs.

Below are the key anatomical locations or areas that should be considered when starting any pain medication to avoid major side effects. The last three areas (Nucleus Accumbens, Frontal Lobe, and Sexual Functioning/ Libido) are often overlooked in primary care pain management. Below each anatomical location is the medicine (type) and its major side effects:

STOMACH
NSAIDs—Gastric ulcers, Bleeding

KIDNEYS
NSAIDs—Acute Renal Failure, Renal Tubular Acidosis

MEDULLA OBLONGATA
Opiates—Respiratory Failure, Overdose

NUCLEUS ACCUMBENS
Opiates—Addiction

FRONTAL LOBE
Opiates—Depression/mood lability

SEXUAL FUNCTIONING/LIBIDO

Opiates—Erectile dysfunction/low testosterone

Anti-depressants—Anorgasmia (male/female)

STOMACH

NSAIDS increase the risk of bleeding significantly in patients with ulcers. If a provider has ever seen someone vomiting blood (hematemesis) due to a bleeding ulcer, they will never forget to consider ulcers when initiating this basic over-the-counter medicine. Trust me, it's not pretty . . .

KIDNEYS

NSAIDS can cause acute kidney injury (AKI); electrolyte and acid-base disorders; acute interstitial nephritis (AIN), which may be accompanied by nephrotic syndrome. So, if your patients have kidney problems, consider an alternative or a very *low* dose.

MEDULLA OBLONGATA

The Medulla Oblongata is a highly specialized part of the brain stem, where the respiratory center is located. Opiates (heroin, fentanyl, oxycodone, hydrocodone, codeine, and others) decrease the function of this area, causing a diminished drive to breathe. Therefore, many opiate-*naïve* patients overdose and die instantly from respiratory failure. Opiate-naïve patients are loosely defined as people that have *never* been on opiates or have been off their opiates for approximately two weeks. What does this mean clinically? Restarting someone on their "regular dose" of opiates, after an opiate hiatus for two weeks, can cause accidental death by acute overdose. Side note: These patients won't be happy when you tell them that you will be starting them on a lower dose than when they discontinued it last. Just be ready.

THE NUCLEUS ACCUMBENS

The Nucleus Accumbens (NAc), located in the basal forebrain, is significantly associated with motivation, reward (i.e., incentive, pleasure, and positive reinforcement), and reinforcement learning; hence, its role in addiction. Its primary purpose is to release dopamine—the major pleasure chemical (neurotransmitter) that makes you want to go back for more, again and again. Here is a visual:

Think of the NAc as the casino in the brain, where the slot machines are the drugs (opiates, cigarettes, alcohol, sex, food), and the winning coins are dopamine. When you first go to the slots, you win 1,000 dopamine coins. Jackpot! Behaviorally, you are positively reinforced to pull the lever again to attain the high you felt the first time. Psychologically, since you won on the first pull, you return to see if it will hit again. Physically, the sensation that overcame your body from the thrill, makes you want to go back for more. On the next pull, sadly, you only win 995 dopamine coins. You are excited, but not as excited as when you hit the jackpot, so you return hoping to get the same payout (high) that you did the first time—it WILL NEVER hit 1,000 again (true story). So, you try to chase the high by increasing your odds of getting a jackpot by playing two slot machines at a time (increasing the dose of the same drug or doing multiple drugs). Nope. No jackpot.

Tolerance is defined as a diminished response to a drug, requiring more of it to get the same effect. If someone's biological makeup is genetically predisposed to addiction, increased exposure to a drug makes addiction almost inevitable.

THE FRONTAL LOBE

It's unclear how opiates cause depression—we just know they do. Most depression occurs within the frontal lobe. Some may say, especially with short-acting opiates (Norco, Vicodin, Oxycodone), that the constant up-and-down fluctuations of the brain's biochemistry disrupt homeostasis leading to a labile mood affect. While similar theories state, "[opiates] create a temporary feeling of *euphoria* followed by *dysphoria* that can easily lead to physical dependence and addiction." Other research suggests that "opioid-induced resetting of the brain's 'reward pathway' to a higher level can elevate the threshold *(make it more difficult)* for a person's ability to experience pleasure from natural rewards such as food or sexual activity."

SEXUAL INTIMACY/LIBIDO

Erectile dysfunction is a common issue with long-term opiate use. Once again, we don't know the exact mechanism, but it may be related to decreasing testosterone levels from the opiates themselves. Or the psychological aspect of chronic pain leading to depression or anhedonia (a lack of enjoyment in things one normally used to find pleasurable). Erectile dysfunction (ED) is a multi-dimensional diagnosis, where over 90% of the cases are psychological. Adding chronic pain and the pain cycle to the ED equation doesn't pan out well for the chronic opiate user. For this reason, it is highly integral that the provider connects and builds rapport with their patients on opiates, who have ED, so that they can discuss issues around erections, masturbation, ejaculation, and intercourse.

Other medications like SSRIs (Selective Serotonin Reuptake Inhibitors) frequently cause anorgasmia (the inability or difficulty in reaching orgasm) in both men and women.

In 2020, over 142 million prescriptions were written, representing approximately 43 prescriptions for every 100 people (which is a decrease from prior years). Further, drug overdoses were responsible for 91,799 deaths in 2020, representing a 70% increase over the prior 12 years. Opioid addiction is driving this epidemic, with 68,330 overdose deaths related to prescription pain relievers and 13,165 overdose deaths related to heroin in 2015."

So, what is the provider's role in treatment? Pain, whether emotional or physical, is a challenging condition to treat; I believe if we follow certain principles, we can make a difference. I created this mnemonic, which has been helpful for me:

"SELF HHELP"

Street smarts
Education
Limit Use
Follow-up

—

Honesty
Ask for **Help**

STREET SMARTS

A physician who prescribes opiates cannot be naïve. We need to know what medications are being sold on the street to avoid prescribing drugs that will be sold illegally. *Promethazine*/Codeine (street name: Lean), a common narcotic-based cough syrup, has a higher street value than *Guaifenesin*/Codeine because the *promethazine*-containing syrup tastes like candy. Therefore, its street use is preferred for mixing it with soda to get *"you-straight-up trippin' as long as you steady sippin'."* According to a recent study by the International Journal of Psychological Studies in 2020, "Purple Drank, Sizurp, and Lean: Hip-Hop Music and Codeine Use, A Call to Action for Public Health Educators,"[36] over 40 hip-hop or rap songs referred to *Lean* and the authors continue to be concerned and curious if this will have any significant impact on Lean's use in the public, especially our younger generation.

An eight-ounce bottle can be sold for up to $200 on the street! That's a huge profit if your prescription copay is $15. *Oxycodone 15mg* has less street value than the

Oxycodone 30mg dose (which is used for crushing and sniffing). I've had plenty of patients who were selling medications that I prescribed. Sadly, I found out second-hand from the seller's friend (also my patient), whom she pissed off. Whoops.

Recently, potent prescription opiate medications like fentanyl are being combined with heroin to make a new drug, which is significantly more potent than heroin itself. It doesn't take much for an opiate addicted, let alone, opiate-naïve person to die within seconds of its injection. Narcan, the medicine that reverses opiates in your body, rarely work for this deadly cocktail.

To avoid abuse, misuse, and drug-seeking behaviors, keep your eyes and ears open and do your best to bring awareness to your biases.

EDUCATION

Time to take some continuing education on opiate use and proper prescribing techniques to avoid over-dose. Understanding the basics of what opiate-naïve means can severely lessen the risk of accidental overdose (which could likely be iatrogenic—caused by medical treatment). In addition, there are many things that we can learn from our patients about the use, misuse and street value of these meds. I know this conversation can feel awkward, but you may be surprised how easy it is when broached with non-judgment and curiosity.

LIMIT USE

This is self-explanatory. Don't give more meds than needed. If you are seeing a patient and don't expect a follow-up, offer a limited number of pills, consider a lower dose and recommend following up with their PCP. It's critical to try and use the lowest effective dose not just for opiates but for *everything*.

FOLLOW UP

As mentioned above, if you are seeing a patient in an urgent care setting and don't expect to follow up, limit the use, and have them follow up with their PCP. When it's my patient and I initiate a new opiate prescription, I only give two weeks to start and encourage follow up to assess how well it's working and how my patient is tolerating it. Close follow-up also lowers the risk of morbidity and mortality, ensures proper use, and encourages a more trusting relationship.

HONESTY

Isn't this everything? Discussions about abuse and misuse are essential in every conversation with a patient who is continuing or starting on narcotic pain medications. Having this open dialog about your boundaries as a physician, when done mindfully, will convey competency while earning trust. When your patients do not feel judged or shamed, they will be first to tell you that they ran out early and had to use extra or needed more, so they bought some on the street or gave some to a friend who was in pain. It happens. This isn't the time to play ethical police. It's time to reconfirm boundaries and, if needed, revisit or introduce the narcotic-use agreement, which deals with lost prescriptions, stolen prescriptions, or meds that were flushed or happen to fall down the drain *"accidentally."*

HELP

One of the biggest lessons I learned in residency was "know what I don't know." There's no room for assumptions and guessing when it comes to our patient's health. I had to get out of my own way, drop my ego and accept that I can't know everything. Asking for input or a "curbside consult" also builds trust and rapport with the one you're asking. Embracing humility made it easier to care for my patients and kept them safer.

Uncomfortable? Well, That's a Start.

"Learn to convert the discomfort . . . into the satisfaction of personal growth."

— Tony Robbins

IF DOCTORS CONTINUE MEDICATING patients to eliminate their emotional suffering, then when will patients ever have a chance to challenge themselves to rise above it on their own? We can't put all the responsibility on the physician, patients carry the responsibility for their own personal growth. Whether it's inquiring about treatment options or disclosing their psychological symptoms, the burden must lie on them first and foremost.

Sadly, some people suffer significant amounts of anxiety and panic regardless of short-term abortive medications. For them, long term medication may be the answer. I don't know anyone who enjoys discomfort, but sometimes it's a doorway into growth:

My wife and I were going through a rough patch, more like the whole quilt. We didn't argue, yell or call each other nasty names, but resentments and frustrations were at an all-time high. We had just come back from a concert in Santa Barbara the night before. We woke up the following morning and came together outside as we always did to have some coffee. Jenn was quiet. The air was eerily still. She said, "We need to talk." "Okay, about what?" I said nervously, thinking, "A 'let's talk' moment is usually not good." She said softly, "I think we should get a divorce." A knife-like sensation pierced my heart, "Oh." I said in shock staring off for a while. She explained her reasons quite well, and to be honest, I think I might have divorced myself too. For years, I was just angry inside, which was masking a deeper sadness from things I hadn't worked through.

We sat there and had a very calm, loving discussion. We decided I would leave the house until we sorted things out. I left terribly sad and went to see a life-long friend for support. I returned home late that night. The next day I made a call and arranged for a place to stay with a friend, to whom I owe a great debt of gratitude. Jenn was crying on the bed as I was packing my belongings. I tried to keep my 5-year-old out of the room while I did this. But she saw. When I finished packing most of my clothes, I entered the hallway, and she was standing there looking up at me and said in her sweet, innocent voice, "Where are you going, daddy?" As my heart filled my throat, I came down to one knee and hugged her feeling like it was the last time I would hug her as a family. "It's okay, baby," I said as I held back the tears. "I'm just going away for a little while, and I will see you soon." "Okay, daddy," she said, as she hugged my neck very tightly. I stood up with tears overflowing my eyelids. I told Jenn, "I love you," and I walked out to my car.

When I got into my car, my first thought was, "What will this teach me?" It surprised me. I knew that if I ruminated for too long, got swallowed up by the bedroom walls, drank too much alcohol, or wallowed in the depressing sensations that I was feeling, I would go down the rabbit hole. Or maybe I was already at the bottom of the rabbit hole and the only place to go was up? Either way, it was my bottom. The suffering I felt was excruciating. I knew in the midst of my misery, there was something to learn. Over the next three weeks I spent away from home, I did some soul searching and found the lesson: I am not my past. I am not the little boy that didn't get his needs met. Stop taking it out on your wife! This awareness is what brought me back home, brought healing to both of us, and allowed us to finally experience a marriage that both of us have wanted since we both said, "I do."

The suffering had its purpose. I found meaning through my intense suffering. It built confidence, self-respect, and self-worth—in other words, I was *aligning my rings,* as stated earlier in this book.

Eckhart Tolle refers to the end of his own suffering in the Introduction to *The Power of Now:*

> . . . *I realized that the acute suffering I felt that night must have forced my consciousness to withdraw from identification with the unhappy self, the suffering "little me," which is ultimately a fiction of the mind. This withdrawal must have been so complete that the suffering self collapsed as if the plug had been pulled out of an inflatable toy. What was left was my true nature as the ever present "I AM": consciousness in its pure state prior to identification with form. You may also call it pure awareness or presence.*

Suffering is perpetuated by discomfort and rarely abates without awareness and action. With medicines like benzodiazepines (Xanax, Ativan, Valium) being prescribed at record numbers, maybe it's time to rethink how they are prescribed. Commonly, a patient will come in and ask for medication to help with their "nerves" or "anxiety." Then it happens: The doctor gives a nice platitude, "Just breathe." Strike one! Unless the provider coaches the patient about proper breathing techniques, their request to "just breathe" misses the mark. While most physicians are doing a good job minimizing controlled substances, many fail to educate themselves about benzodiazepine dependence. Strike two! Lastly, while it is great that providers are limiting these prescriptions, few take it a step further by inviting their patients to explore their symptoms in context with their life situation. Strike three:

Kathy, a 37-year-old female came to my office to discuss anxiety. "Hi Kathy, nice to see you again. What's up?" "Thanks, Dr. Mike. I'm going through a really tough situation at home and on the verge of a panic attack every day." "I'm so sorry, what's going on Kathy?" "Well, my husband and I are overwhelmed with bills, we may lose our house, and I'm so worried for my kids that we won't have anywhere to live. It's really overwhelming. I'm not even sleeping but four hours per night," she said as tears started to roll down her cheek. "That sounds tough," I said empathically, "Are you doing anything to keep calm?" "No," as she wiped her tears, "I was hoping you could help me with that. I used a friend's Ativan twice per day for the last week and I felt so much better. I was hoping you could give me a prescription." I looked down, "Hmmm, I hear you. No doubt it sounds like you are overwhelmed. I would probably be as well, but I wouldn't feel right giving you a full prescription of Ativan. I would be happy to give you a few, so you can use them when it's just too much, but not to use daily or frequently." She begged, "I know, Dr. Lewis, but I'm just so overwhelmed." "Kathy, you may not like what I'm going to say, but please hear me. These meds are dangerous and addictive. I think it's important to remember that discomfort can help us gain the confidence to remember how resilient we are. I would be doing you a disservice if I simply wrote you a script and told you to take these twice a day when you feel overwhelmed. You'll have to trust me on this. I've seen it many times. Look, I want to help you. I am happy to give you 15 pills . . ." I said, as she interrupted, "Thanks Dr. Lewis, but that's not good enough! So . . . what? I'm just supposed to suffer here?" "I am willing to give you some, but I hate to say it, yes, a little bit. If it becomes too much, you can take a half or whole pill," I said. With her arms folded, she scoffed and said, "Are we done? Please send my prescription to my pharmacy." She stomped out of the room and slammed the door behind her.

There are many ways I could've handled this. A paternalistic approach to medicine seemed appropriate in this instance. It's our duty to provide our knowledge, foresight, and experience to educate and hold necessary boundaries with our patients. We should be able to make tough decisions with a clear conscience. Hopefully the lessons we give our patients plant a seed in their psyche to be cultivated in the future or at minimum save them from themselves.

To complicate matters, the DEA (Drug Enforcement Agency) has significantly cracked down on controlled substance prescriptions. Our license is on the line more than ever, which means more government oversight controlling our management.

We can't please everyone, but a physician's job, contrary to popular belief, *isn't* to. What appears to be insensitive may just be good medicine. We must make tough decisions even when we think the outcome of our relationship may become strained; being liked isn't more important than our patient's safety.

I felt great compassion for Kathy's circumstance and how bad it might feel to have those burdens weighing her down. As we saw in Kathy's case, the worry was overwhelming, causing sleep and mood lability. The choice *not to* medicate her ultimately was a merciful one, not only because the medication is addictive, but because

I felt it was important to help and try to empower Kathy through her anxieties without needing pharmaceutical help. As human beings who like to avoid suffering, we rarely have the patience to sit with our discomfort when a pill could stop it dead in its tracks.

This pattern of using substances as a substitute for self-soothing can start early, grossly retarding one's emotional and developmental maturity. Early, chronic marijuana use or benzodiazepines can stunt this process, freezing them at the stage they began using.

Confidence comes with overcoming challenges.

The lessons we all can learn from overcoming difficult situations is invaluable and as medical providers, proposing alternative perspectives to our patients may provide valuable opportunities for personal growth. But one should be careful not to sound patronizing, which is why I tend to save conversations like the one I had with Kathy, for relationships with an established rapport.

THREE IS YOUR NEW ZERO

"Please rate your pain on a zero to ten scale. Zero being no pain, ten being I just force-fed you live scorpions then ripped off both of your arms."

— Unknown

IT IS OFTEN SAID THAT LOW EXPECTATIONS help keep us from disappointment. In the case of pain, a discussion on expectations is imperative in the planning of chronic management. The reason is that many people who are being treated for chronic pain *expect* their pain to diminish to zero after treatment with medications. Unfortunately, this isn't always the case.

Patients often come to see me with a history of car accidents, falls from ladders, and other serious injuries that have been self-treated with over-the-counter (OTC) meds for some time without significant resolution of their pain. They may have difficulties sleeping and become irritable and depressed because their pain isn't well-managed, who wouldn't? A physician's job is to simultaneously assess the appropriateness of the patient to be treated with opiods and to provide education and expectations for pain control. If the patient comes in with an eight out of 10 pain (on a scale where 10 is the worst pain), I *wouldn't* expect my medications to give this patient complete resolution of their symptoms, nor would I want to give false hope that it would. If anything, it would be better to underplay the potential for improvement, *"you may get a little improvement,"* so that if the pain surpasses my minimized expectation, they will be much happier and more inclined to continue (under-promise and over-deliver).

It's tough to be a healer when patients suffer from debilitating, chronic, daily pain, knowing we most likely won't be able to *"cure"* them. The cycle of pain is multifactorial, and it's important to approach treatment from all directions, starting with a good history, physical, and one key question: "What is your expectation in treating your pain?" They may say, "I'm just looking to sleep better because the pain keeps me up all night." Or they may tell you, "I'm looking to eliminate my pain altogether!" If a patient's expectation differs from the practitioner's, it will be almost impossible to agree on the proper therapy. Therefore, it's crucial to spend time getting to know the patient, feel them out, and facilitate a collaborative relationship. Once there is common ground, the conversation about pain management can move forward. Plenty of times, expectations for pain control aren't discussed, and patients return to the office frustrated that they still have pain:

Barry is a 33-year-old male hockey player who came into my office to discuss his recurrent pain. He had a family history of opiate dependence. "Hi Barry, welcome back. How can I help you today?" "Hey, Dr. Lewis, I wanted to come to talk to you about my pain," he stated. "Go on," I said (with a wave of my hand). "Well, for years, I have had headaches and chronic muscle aches which come and go. I take an occasional Oxy, but I don't like doing that. So, I take about four grams of Tylenol most days." I asked, "Does the medicine help?" "Yes," he nodded. "On a scale of one to 10, where 10 is the worst pain, how would you rank yours?" I asked. He looked up to think and said, "On a bad day, eight. On a good day, five." "Okay, have there been any injuries?" I questioned. "Shit, I'm a hockey player, doc. I've had a hockey puck bust my left orbit, I've lost these teeth," he points to the upper teeth, "I've broken my arm, different fingers, my left shin bone. I'm a mess, man." "Shit man, what do you do for work?" I asked. "I'm in construction." I continued, "So you do lots of heavy lifting and manual labor?" "Of course," he said. After some more interviewing, we moved on to treatment options, and I said, "Here's what I would like to do, Barry. Let's give you a trial of an anti-inflammatory that focuses on the bones and joints, so it's easier on your stomach. Take one per day and see me in a week to discuss how you are doing. How does that sound?" "I was hoping for something a little stronger, but I'm open. You're the doc," he stated, seemingly disappointed.

One week later, Barry returned for follow-up. "So, Barry. How are you doing? Did the medicine help?" I asked with a hopeful tone. "Nah, doc. Maybe a touch, but not really. I'm still having pain all the time." I already had a plan in place if this medicine didn't work, so I moved forward, "I do not want to give you a heavy narcotic because of your family history. But I do have something that I think will work well for you. Most people tolerate it great without any side effects." "What is it?" he asked curiously. I said, "Tramadol." "I've taken it, and it gives me headaches," he claimed. "I hear you. That could've been the manufacturer. That's a rare side effect, and if you get it, it should go away within a week or two, so please give it a try." He shrugged his shoulders, "Okay." "One more thing," I added, "I want you to understand that your pain may never go away completely. I hope it does, but I want you to have reasonable expectations. You are very hard on your body, and unless you ease up, your pain will continue." He interrupted, "I'm not going to stop." "I didn't think so, so what would be a reasonable pain level to function on your good days and worst days?" I asked. He said bluntly, "At least three and five." "Okay then, that's a good start. Come back in two weeks and let me know how you are doing," we shook hands and he left.

Two weeks later, he returned. "Hey, Barry . . . So?" I asked. "Pain is much better," he said. "Headaches?" I questioned. "Nope, just as you said," he snapped his fingers, "after a week, they went away." "And your pain level?" He said, "About a five at its worst and a zero to two depending on what I'm doing." "Great, Barry, let's continue the meds and follow up soon. I'm so happy to hear this!" He left the office satisfied.

In Barry's case, treatment expectations were discussed, and the outcome was positive. I planned for alternatives should my initial suggestions fail to get his pain under control *(I do have something that I think will work well for you)*. I also tried to help curb his possible fear of persistent headaches from the medication *(I hear you. That could've been the manufacturer)*. Never underestimate the effectiveness of a thorough discussion.

HIDE AND GO SEEK

"It's wabbit season, and I'm hunting wabbits, so be vewy, vewy quiet!"

— Elmer Fudd

NOT EVERYONE WHO COMES INTO THE OFFICE looking for pain meds is an addict, nor should they be treated like one. Before the patient has ever been seen for *pain* or *a refill of pain meds*, it's not uncommon that the patient is pigeon-holed into being a drug-seeker by the clinician solely based on the chief complaint noted in the schedule. This isn't to say that there aren't plenty of *drug-seekers.* Our "narcotic-seeking-radar" should be pinging when someone arrives asking for a "pain med refill." However, the real issue is the constant judgment among physicians towards these types of patients. Each patient is an individual. Let us not forget our humanity, no matter our role as an expert, in these interactions.

Similarly, with mental health complaints, pain and pain medication refill patients are often cast aside and marginalized. People *do* have pain. People *do* have opiate dependency. People *do* need refills. To avoid biases in these situations, a physician must use their instincts, experience, and street smarts while balancing compassion, empathy, and good medicine (evidenced-based and experience-based).

All the answers you need will be presented to you during the interview. Between body language, history of medication use and allergies you will be able to get a good picture of what's *really* going on without making the patient feel like a criminal. Of note, many people with drug-seeking behavior claim to have "allergies" to *all* over-the-counter medications and weaker opiates.

As physicians, it's easy to get all riled up when a drug-seeker comes into your office and tries to manipulate you into giving them what they want by contriving a ridiculous story: "*All* of my pills fell down the drain." But it's not our job to be judge and jury. It's our job to keep our patients safe while they are in our care, and sometimes that means denying their requests.

Physicians and other healthcare personnel *need* (I don't use this word often) to stop judging and shaming patients who suffer from chronic pain and opiate dependence. It's corrosive and interferes with patients' welfare. Addicts are suffering. Addicts are under the thumb of chemical dependency. They aren't less than, they are trapped. Manipulation and conflict are symptoms of their addiction and can be frustrating. Maintaining a compassionate stance is challenging, but it's possible.

PART TEN

DIRECT PRIMARY CARE
CONCIERGE MEDICINE

THE DOCTOR HAS LEFT THE BUILDING

"The doctor of the future will give no medication, but will interest his patients in the care of the human frame, diet and in the cause and prevention of disease."

— Thomas Edison

WHAT DOES IT LOOK LIKE WHEN YOU'VE JUST HAD ENOUGH? I spent the last 20 years practicing medicine and honing my skills to get where I am now. When I was a newer doctor, I dealt with the bureaucracy and other bullshit that came with the field because that was part of the job.

I admire clinicians working hard in the corporate medical world. It's a good gig, though at times it was soul-sucking and thankless.

To be honest, I feel a little envious of the doctors that can hang in there for the long haul. Sometimes, I wish I could have. The real issue here is complacency. After a while some physicians get frustrated, fed-up, burned out, and complain, yet are too complacent to make a change. Why? Let's try to recognize a few reasons:

Fear . . .
Fear of losing their home
Fear of not being able to pay the bills
Fear of change
Fear of the unknown
Fear of trusting themselves
Fear of disappointing their family
Fear of putting their family at risk

In my case, I didn't feel like I had a choice. I was in an existential crisis, a crossroads compelling me to take a different path. The ensuing depression and angst were taking their toll on my family. My patients were suffering the wrath of my exasperation. This wasn't acceptable to anyone, especially me, and many patients were being affected by this.

It became especially apparent when a beloved patient said to me: *"Dr. Mike, are you alright? Because you were a real asshole the last time I saw you."* That was a reality check. It was time to move on, but I had to do it pragmatically. Though I wasn't fearful of change in general, I was afraid of the financial burden that leaving this job would present. Gratefully, I had a pension that would soon be 100% vested, so I had to suck it up until then. It was the ticket to get us through lack of income until I figured out my next move. Then as the 2014 calendar year ended, I was expecting a financial bonus (as shareholders for HMOs receive multiple times per year) and was shocked to learn that it was shorted by over $20,000. I was appalled. Appalled doesn't even do it justice. I was pissed off. These bonuses were critical to stabilize our income for the coming months. I'd had it up to here (holding my hand way above my head). You know the saying, the straw that broke the camel's back? Can you guess who the camel was? Luckily, my broken back didn't affect my determination. I called a large bank on Thursday, January 5, 2015, to inquire about a loan to open my own concierge/direct primary care (DPC) medical practice.

My world was about to change.

I was never more anxious, sad, or frustrated during the next two months while awaiting the loan decision. I prayed for anything to silence my mind. I was so *gone* that even my frequent meditation routine, that I wasn't very good at, was useless to quell the enormous anxiety within me. The Auscultation Meditation was forgotten. Let's just say I played lots of *Candy Crush* to distract myself. A glimmer of hope came when I received a phone call from my banker. He said, *"Dr. Lewis, after all*

DIRECT PRIMARY CARE CONCIERGE MEDICINE

the bullshit we have been through, the underwriters are going to approve your loan." I was beyond excited. My wife, Jenn and I drank champagne, laughed, clinked glasses, and no shit, an hour later, the cellphone rang. It was my banker, *"I'm sorry, Doctor Lewis, but the underwriters have decided not to approve your loan after all."* Deflated yet determined, I didn't give up that easily. I reached out to two more banks and was approved within three weeks.

Holy shit! Amazing!

Then, sadly, my wife and I separated. Another gut-punch. The time apart was some of the most challenging times I had experienced up to that point. I was still trying to build the practice on paper, create orders, corporations, contact attorneys and make lists while trying to save my marriage. I spent lots of time in solitude to reflect and own my responsibility in my failing marriage. After three weeks, we reconciled. With renewed honestly and authentic connection, we were stronger than we had ever been in the eight years we were married. Ironically, the separation was the best thing that could have happened to us. Whew. With a newly found determination, I cultivated the birth of my dream medical office while having my wife, Dr. Jenn, work directly down the hall as the in-house psychologist.

We named it: *Willow Healing Center*

The Doctor Is In

"People do not decide to become extraordinary. They decide to accomplish extraordinary things."

— Edmund Hillary

BANK DEPOSIT MADE. CORPORATION PAPERWORK FILED. About a million tiny details later, 263 Candy Crush levels passed, two bottles of champagne, a marriage separation, a marriage reconciliation, three gallons of tears, a bit less hair, a few more pounds, a shit-ton of gauze, a new set of keys and it was time to open my own practice.

The idea was simple: Work for my patients, not the bureaucracy, and deliver personalized care while not having to rush through each visit like I'm trying to escape a fire. Goals: pay attention to the *entire* patient (*whole-*istic); make psychological services available in-house; deliver high-quality medical care; and offer a simple, no-hassle membership with a variety of convenient amenities:

- An affordable monthly membership fee

- 24/7 access
- Same-day appointments
- No copays or deductibles
- 100+ wholesale medications filled on-site
- Free procedures
- Long appointment times
- Limit the number of patients to less than 80% of the typical 3,500 patients most doctors see

Naïvely, I figured all I had to do now was open the doors and bam! A full panel in no time. Boy was I wrong. Willow's ribbon cutting was on August 10, 2015 and we signed up a whopping two new patients. It was scary given that I thought I would have at least 2% of the 3,000 patients from my previous job–60 patients. That wasn't the case. As Willow became known in the community, a slight buzz began to happen, and more people were calling and setting up appointments. Still, understanding this model was the most challenging obstacle to signups: *"What is concierge medicine/direct primary care?"* I learned that the majority of the community is unaware of this fantastic model of medicine. Some have been introduced to this model from the television show *The Royal Pains*, which depicted a traveling house-call concierge doctor who only tended to the affluent suburbs of the

Hamptons. In fact, concierge medicine was classically available only to the rich and famous, garnering a reputation for pandering to the wealthy. With Willow, this wasn't the case, as I was offering my services at a meager price of less than $100 per month, and since I didn't bill insurance, we didn't need to hire a biller or hire a large staff—I didn't even have a nurse, ever. It was me and Jenn, always. I thought educating the public about Concierge Medicine/Direct Primary Care as a low-cost alternative without sacrificing care would give me the keys to the kingdom. I did local and international TV news spots, I had a huge article in the LA Times newspaper, I joined the chamber of commerce and gave talks and became part of a small business group, I even had a YouTube channel doing medical procedures, which cultivated over 16,000 subscribers and seven million views.

With the *un*-Affordable Care Act having rising costs and sky-rocketing deductibles, I faced common questions such as, "Why would I join you if I already have insurance?" or "My premiums are so high, how can I afford you?"

The reality is with the *un*ACA, 27% of Californians joining the exchange with a Bronze-level plan have deductibles of $6,000 per year per individual, and 64% of Californians with a Silver plan have deductibles of

$2,000 and higher[37]—one cannot afford *not* to have me. Why? We know that 80% of patients with a deductible of $5,000 or more never reach it, which means most costs are out of pocket.

So, for less than half the cost of the yearly deductible, people could have a compassionate, private doctor who cares more about his patients than appeasing the insurance companies. A doctor who can finally take the time to get to know his patients on a deeper level without the time limitations of an HMO or traditional models of medicine. Patients were sick and tired of the same old medical bureaucratic bullshit; frankly, so was I. I thought the timing was perfect. This style of medicine fills in the deficiencies that traditional practices left behind—time, relationships, same-day appointments, unhurried visits, cost transparency, and personalized care.

In July 2016, I went away with my family to Alaska for seven days. Though I had another local physician covering me for office visit emergencies, I still made myself available for phone calls and questions. It is gratifying that when cruising through the icebergs of the Northern Pacific, I can receive text messages from patients, talk to them about their symptoms, treat their infection, and fax an antibiotic to their local pharmacy, all from the comfort of the 15th deck, enjoying a glass of "water" with my feet up. Life was good. It felt like I hoped it would all those years back in medical school.

I went into family medicine because my love for people and medicine created an ideal outlet for my talents. Studying medicine was more about relationships and the overall health of the patient, a far cry from the reality of HMO care. Sadly, the traditional model of medicine, what we are all used to, has reprioritized the patient-doctor relationship into the patient-clock relationship.

A typical day in the life of a concierge doc isn't like it is in mainstream corporate medicine. It was dull at times. To be honest, I wrote much of this book during my working office hours at Willow. My days varied as far as the patient volume went. Some days I saw no patients; on others, I saw eight—half of them were there for refills. The beautiful part about this way of practicing is that my patients are never booked for less than 45 minutes. If they only need five minutes, that's fine, but if they need more, they've got it. New patient appointments are typically one and a half hours, most of the time spent getting to know one another and taking a good medical history. Ironically, some patients would say, "Dr. Mike, I really need to get out of here. How much longer?"

Obviously, I had no trouble transitioning.

My office was set up to be a soothing and relaxing

environment—was luxurious but not pretentious. It had a homey-feel to it that Jenn and I designed while we were binge-watching our favorite show at the time, *House of Cards*.

White coat hypertension begins when patients walk into medical offices, so we did what we could to make the environment calming and beautiful, filled with soothing scents and ambient music (though often we played Bob Marley). We had a *healing room* where sometimes I meditated with my clients, burned sage with intention, used it as a quiet space for patients to chill out, or for other practitioners that joined Willow, such as reiki masters, chiropractors, and acupuncturists.

I had a lab where I could do treadmill stress testing, EKGs, lung volume testing, minor surgeries, intravenous fluids, microscopy, and a medical dispensary, where I bottled, labeled, and filled over 120 medications while patients waited, saving them a trip to the pharmacy. In-office dispensing is about convenience and cost savings. Therefore, my medications were priced just above wholesale cost.

All my visits started (after vital signs) in my office, just talking and catching up on life. To honestly treat and care for my patients, I believed I should get to know them, just as they should get to know me. This trust and rapport enriched the visit, and set the tone for a collaborative working relationship.

Primary care is undergoing a massive paradigm shift, as evidenced by changing trends in the last decade. As of January 2015, there were approximately 5,000 concierge practices in the United States, representing a substantial growth from the low numbers in 2004. This increase in Concierge/DPC practices likely represents the transition of seasoned physicians away from typical insurance-based practices, as seen by the dwindling number of physicians entering a residency in primary care. The University of California, San Diego (UCSD) recently graduated 164 medical students; only four of the graduates entered a family practice residency—a massive shift from the past where 20% of a graduating class would go into family practice. In 2016, only five students graduating from the University of California, Irvine, were matriculating into a family medicine residency. The American Association of Medical Colleges (AAMC) predicted a 91,000-physician shortage in 2020. It's not a coincidence that this trend persists, given the strangle-hold placed upon today's primary care physicians.

One argument that anti-concierge/DPC critics (yes, there is such a thing) believe is that the growth of concierge medicine/DPC will exacerbate the physician shortage because it's taking away doctors from the

traditional pools of providers. I believe the contrary—
Concierge medicine/DPC is going to save primary care. The
problem doesn't just lie with the doctors, the corporations, or the government alone; it's a multifactorial
issue that needs significant reform. But wait, didn't we
just have healthcare reform with the Unaffordable Care
Act? Hell no! Do you want to talk about what's leading to
the shortage of physicians? Here, I give you a
government-run healthcare field that's increasing the
number of the patient pool by a staggering 30 million,
while the number of doctors is declining rapidly.[38]

THE DOCTOR IS OUT

"Success is not final; failure is not fatal: It is the courage to continue that counts."

— Winston Churchill

SADLY, THREE YEARS INTO my concierge medicine/DPC practice—ironically on Doctors' Day—Willow closed. I had 105 patients, and no matter how much marketing I did and how many local and international news appearances I made, Willow hit a ceiling. For perspective, I needed 95 patients to pay the bills. Jenn and I went to a local winery and had a serious discussion about the future of Willow and the decision to close. It was a wonderful talk. Jenn was impressively supportive and understanding that it was my dream to open this practice and was willing to see it through the tough times to support it.

I knew what I had to do before we poured our first glass of Syrah.

I made a clear, ego-less decision to close the practice. I didn't feel defeated or like a failure. I had faced fear and complacency in the eyes and had taken on a new challenge. I didn't minimize the success of Willow just because we had to close. After all, I measured the success of Willow not from the number of patients or how long Willow was open but from the journey of overcoming my personal and logistical barriers. I've always said there is no growth in complacency. What a ride.

Fortuitously, the same week Jenn and I decided to close Willow, my good friend Paolo, who was the medical director at the urgent care where I was moonlighting said, "Dude. When are you going to come work at the prison?" In past conversations, he'd asked me this same question, but this time, I was free for a new challenge and adventure. Timing is everything, isn't it?

I immediately put in an application via the Corrections website, and within two weeks, I had an interview. I was hired shortly after, mainly because Paolo had an outstanding reputation with the management, and they trusted his judgment. After about eight weeks, I started my new path of working at a Level-4, maximum security prison. Within 30 days of my starting, I applied to be Chief Physician and was hired. Thank you, Paolo.

Willow was now in my past, but the experiences of

owning, starting, building, and running a medical practice remain a precious part of my life's journey.

PART ELEVEN

DOCTORS BEHIND BARS

A VIEW IS WORTH
1,000 WORDS

*"If you want total security, go to prison. There, you're
fed, clothed, given medical care and so on. The only
thing lacking . . . is freedom."*

— Dwight D. Eisenhower

IN THE BLINK OF AN EYE, my view changed from my
comfortable pristine, home-like office to the pale tan
walls of my new office facing Bravo (B) yard. I was
ready—I watched every episode of *Locked-up Raw,*

Locked-up Abroad, Goodfellas, and *American Me*—What else did I need? For the next three years of my life, I worked in the Corrections system as the Chief Physician. I spent most of my time behind a desk while patient interactions were limited to 0-10% of my week. The other fraction of my work was made up supervising my staff of physicians and mid-level providers, running the Utilization Management committee (approving specialists, radiology, etc.), chairing the Reasonable Accommodations committee, running medical clinic operations, justifying visits per day, dealing with office visit backlogs, assessing metrics, ensuring numbers are met, just to name a few. If you haven't figured it out, I was working for an HMO again! Damn it!

I'm laughing at the irony.

The patient population was all male criminals. Twenty-five percent were LWOPs (Serving Life With Out Parole), 25% had Hepatitis C (from alcohol or intravenous drug use—IVDU), and a significant majority were very ill, disabled, or had multiple rheumatic diseases. Traumas were a weekly and sometimes daily occurrence. The fights were so vicious that knife wounds, orbital fractures, and ruptured globes (eyeballs) were frequent. It was a dangerous place for criminals, but not so much for the providers—I'll come back to this later.

When I told people about my new position at a

Level-4 maximum-security prison, I was usually met with excited curiosity, while other times, I was met with concern: Aren't you worried about getting hurt or attacked? How can you treat these people knowing what they've done? Why would someone with your talents work for a prison? All valid questions. After contemplating the concerns people had for me, I made a couple of rules for myself about how I would treat the prisoners:

1. Heed the Hippocratic oath, work with integrity and take care of the inmate/patients.
2. Don't look at the reasons why they are in there.
3. Stay objective.
4. Don't be afraid to connect.

The rules served me well. Numbers 1 and 4 were easy. It was number 3 and its relation to number 2 that "concerned" me. For example, I'd never been face-to-face with a convicted murderer or treated one; I wondered how I would react once I did.

I'm reminded of this child molester from one of the rare days that I saw patients (a sentence I didn't think I would ever say or write). He was convicted of *lewd and lascivious acts* with a 6-year-old girl. He came in complaining of insomnia: "I'm sorry you are having some trouble sleeping, Mr. Molester. As a matter of fact, good, you deserve it. You're a child molester. Go fuck yourself. No pills for you! Enjoy your insomnia with what you've done." Okay, I didn't say a word of that, but to be honest, I'm human and I considered this exact sentence in the moment, but that's not how I work. I treat the *person*, not their criminal history. And frankly, each new challenge in my life is another opportunity to learn what I'm made of. I don't think we truly know ourselves or how we will react to any given situation until we are faced with it.

"Toto, I've Got a Feeling We're not in Kansas Anymore."

— Dorothy, *The Wizard of Oz*

LET ME BE FRANK—some days, I was shocked by what I saw when rounding in our prison hospital.

Retaliation, like nothing I've ever heard of:

In 2016, a 28-year-old Mexican Mafia member, Mr. J was stabbed in the rectum through the anus with a man-made 16-inch prison shank, just to teach him a lesson. The shank was left within Mr. J's rectum until surgeons removed it. The shank perforated his large intestines and spilled the contents into the abdominal cavity, essentially seeding the cavity with blood and feces. He faced over 19 months of surgeries and antibiotics due to multiple complications and septicemia caused by this horrific act of violence. Since the initial incident, he has dropped out of the gang and is still recovering from a recent open wound on his abdomen from yet another abdominal infection.

Enter the FBI (foreign body insertion/ ingestion), another common occurrence:

Mr. U was sent to the TTA (Triage and Treatment Area, aka urgent care) for a Foreign Body Insertion (FBI). He was pissed and wanted to go to the hospital but didn't have a medical reason. Yet. Maybe he wanted better meals, was instructed to pick up a package (drugs) left in the hospital bathroom or was severely mentally ill. Who knows? Nonetheless, he arrived complaining that he had put a pen filler into his urethra. A pen filler is the typical transparent ink-filled tube within all ballpoint pens. We couldn't remove it on site and he had to be sent to the hospital for removal. Unfortunately, this wasn't the first time he had done this, in fact it was the seventh time that month!. He had so much scar tissue from repeating this process, that this time he damaged his urethra from the vigorous force he used to shove it in.

Sometimes, the safety of our own were indeed at risk:

Mrs. N., one of our nurse practitioners, was waiting to see Inmate/patient Mr. L. He was late to the appointment, which doesn't happen too often because they are usually brought to the clinic in groups by custody and locked in a holding cell until they are called for their appointment. This time he wasn't there. Around 10:45 am, I received a call from custody informing me that Mr. L was planning on stabbing our nurse practitioner.

Luckily, Mr. L. had second thoughts and turned himself into custody just minutes before his appointment. He had a prison-made shank with Mrs. N's full name written on it. He was taken to Ad-Seg (Administrative Segregation Unit), the prison's prison, where he awaited a transfer out. I gave Mrs. N. some time off as she was appropriately shaken. She returned to work a couple of days later and started seeing patients again like a pro.

I really understand why prisons were made:

I was walking to see Mr. B. in his cell within Ad-Seg. I was the chair of the Reasonable Accommodations Panel, which ensures inmate/patients receive appropriate accommodations for their disabilities, such as a cane, walker, low-bunk, low-tier, hearing aids, etc.

Mr. B. used a walker and was known to have stabbed an officer about a year prior with parts that he sharpened from his walker. Shockingly, despite this fact, he still had it. Because he was purposefully and consistently damaging his walkers, our committee decided it was time to remove it.

Whenever I approached Ad-Seg, an eerie, dark feeling always overwhelmed me. Inside, it was dimly lit, and the voices of the inmates echoed through all corners of the halls. The gunner was above me— you could see him walking through the areas of thick plexiglass ceiling. I let custody know that I was going to see Mr. B at cell front. They asked if I wanted a chaperone. I declined. I slipped the military green stab-vest over my head and tightened the velcro flank belts. My flanks, groin, chest, abdomen, back, neck, and throat were now protected. I proceeded down to his cell. As I approached his cell front, I noticed liquid pooling on the ground coming from beneath his door; it smelled putrid. I walked to his cell door, avoiding the fluid, and peered in without saying anything. The door was all blue metal with holes so we could hear one another and had a 5" wide window that ran from the top to the bottom of the door. First, I noticed he was sitting on the toilet and had flooded his cell with toilet water. He was barefoot. I remember thinking, "He's not right in the head." His walker was hanging on his wall and missing a leg. He was holding said leg.

(Graphic language below):

I banged on his door. "Mr. B! Hi, I'm Dr. Lewis." While looking down at his hands, he said, "I know who you are. What the fuck do you want?" I said directly, "I'm here to tell you that I'm taking away your walker because you keep dismantling it." He snapped his head to look at me, "I don't use a walker," he said, holding walker parts in his hands. I pointed, "The one on your wall, I'm removing it." He yelled loudly, "You dumb mother-fucker, like hell you are." He stood up, "You can't do that. You fag. You fucker. Fuck you." "Well, Mr. B, I already removed your accommodations, and custody will come by soon to remove it from you." He walked over to the door and stared at me. He was inches from me, thankfully separated by thick steel. Mr. B. said, "You stupid mother fucker, you fag, asshole." He went quiet, and suddenly my thoughts flashed to a dark alley and what would happen to me if this was the outside world. I looked at him directly in the eyes, and goosebumps rapidly covered my body. His eyes were dark, soulless. I couldn't see a separation between his iris and his pupils. I was more than freaked out, to be honest. It was then I knew why prisons were made.

But occasionally, there's a shining light in a room of darkness:

I was seeing patients in my clinic, and Mr. P came in. He was a 45-year-old African American male who had been in prison since he was 18 years old. It's an awe-inspiring moment when you can see true rehabilitation in these men. Mr. P's eyes were bright, curious, and soft. I don't recall why he came in, but we liked each other instantly. He was sitting on the exam table, and I sat on my chair next to him to have a conversation. Somehow, we began chatting about my travels and I mentioned New York (I did my fourth year of medical school at Wyckoff Heights Medical Center in Brooklyn, New York). His eyes lit up like it was Christmas morning. He said longingly, "You've been there? What was it like?" I talked to him about Brooklyn, Manhattan, the subways, and the energy of the city. He was engaged in a way that a little boy might be. He asked, "Where else have you been?" I told him about London, Italy, Sint Maarten, Scotland, and Germany and asked, "Have you been to any of those places?" He responded, "No, man. I've been here since I was 18. I was a little punk that made some stupid decisions. You see, we didn't have summer camps where I came from . . ." I interrupted, "Where did you grow up?" "South central," he continued, "We didn't have summer camps. My world was six square blocks. I had to worry about which streets I would take to school; one way, there were gangs, and the other way was guys from another hood that would jump me if I wasn't careful. I had to hide and move slowly on the way to school. It was dangerous. My family couldn't just pick up and move. This is what I knew. This was my life. It was like I had no choice and got caught up, so here I am."

I think about Mr. J. and sometimes tears come to my eyes, thinking about how impossible it was for him. He had no chance. The man I saw was not the troubled boy who was sent to prison. I would have him over for dinner if I could. He was a remarkable man who will always have a place in my heart.

Mr. J and I embraced, "Until next time, my friend."

Released From Prison

"Nothing is permanent in this wicked world—not even our troubles."

— Charlie Chaplin

IT WAS THURSDAY, MARCH 4, 2021, when I turned in my resignation letter. The following day would be my last day— my parole date if you will.

Honestly, I didn't want to leave, but my work environment felt too hostile to stay. From my vantage point, leadership consisted of micromanaging, power-hungry individuals who were vindictive and hostile to employees they didn't like. The administration, led by one individual, who I will refer to as Joseph Stalin (Joe for short) was known for his tough reputation. If Joe didn't like you, he would make your work life completely miserable. It seemed that he didn't like anyone—but, I hoped for the best.

April 2020 was the beginning of the end. The prison had 250 nurses and 11 medical providers. Covid was starting to spread in our prison and talk of mass testing began. Stalin requested that I send some physicians to Bravo (B) yard to do Covid testing on the 164 inmate/ patients there. As chief, I wasn't happy with this decision and was quite vocal about it. I was called into Joe's office on a Wednesday afternoon:

Walking towards his office, I was curious about my summoning. I didn't think I was in trouble. I walked in, and his key henchmen were there. I sat down and remained quiet. Joe said, "Dr. Lewis, I hear that you don't want the providers to perform Covid testing on the inmates?" I was shaken as I was smack-dab in the middle of the wolf's den. I said, "I don't think the providers should be doing the testing. We have 250 nurses and 11 providers, and we can't afford to lose a medical provider because then we can't run clinics or the hospital." There was silence. I continued, "Let me see if I can explain. Albeit not a great example, but it may help. In war, you don't send the officers to the front line." Joe stopped me instantly. "Come on, Dr. Lewis, in war, when times are tough, the generals are sent to the front lines." I was speechless at this idiocy.

He continued, "So, Dr. Lewis, are you saying that our nurses are expendable and that your physicians are more important than they are?" I thought, a total mischaracterization of my sentiment. "Wait, don't misunderstand me," I said, "that's not what I'm saying at all. We can't run our clinics and the hospital if our providers get sick. That's all. I don't want anyone to get sick." I spent the next 20 minutes making a futile attempt to backtrack while trying to correct the notion that I thought nurses were expendable. It was one snap after another. I remained in a defensive posture until the meeting was over.

It felt horrible to be taken so egregiously out of context, mainly because their interpretation was the furthest thing from my mind; I respected our nurses tremendously; however, to me, it seemed that meeting was the beginning of a campaign to smear my reputation.

Within three weeks, I received my first write-up for my "poor job performance." I've never been written up or told my work was subpar.

Another month passed, and I received a second write-up. All the while, Stalin's henchman continued to find ways to make my life miserable with accusations and workplace bullying.

Due to this, I didn't come out of my office for six weeks except to use the restroom. I was in tears. I was fearful. I was scared my words would be taken out of context and used against me. I was beaten down—I never thought this could happen to me.

I was muzzled by fear and realized I was in an abusive relationship. I've never, in my life, felt anything like this. I thought Joe won.

After many talks with my wife, I found my strength and voice again. I'd had enough.

The dust settled a bit as months went on, but I could still feel the undercurrent of animosity. One day in early February 2021, I received a call from the police of the prison, requesting that I come up to their office.

Little did I know, Joe alleged I committed timesheet fraud (a huge deal) and started an investigation against me. Not coincidentally, he made the allegation in July, just after our meeting. The police interrogated me. It was a nerve-wracking experience—I don't recommend it. After going through this, I knew I had to leave this job because it was becoming too dangerous for me to stay; I figured this was a warning of more sinister things to come.

The allegation was subsequently unsubstantiated.

Fortuitously, seven months before the police investigation, I started looking for other jobs. I wasn't sure what I would do if offered an interview, but I liked the idea of having options. I liked having some control. I liked knowing there was a way out of this abusive environment. It was like Rapunzel feeling hopeful because she could see the world outside her tower.

Oh shit, was I in prison?

A couple of days after my hearing, I received an invitation for a job interview with the local health department. Two weeks later, I was offered the position and accepted it. Five days later, I turned in my resignation notice.

The day before my last day, I emailed the entire staff, notifying them of my resignation. Word spread quickly. On my final day, I walked around the whole prison and said goodbye to everyone I could, including prisoners. Honestly, it was the most humbling experience I have ever had. The things people said about their experiences with me were overwhelming and moving. I went yard to yard, having to wipe away the tears before entering the next one. It was as if I was a fly on the wall at my funeral and was privileged to hear what everyone would say about me. I spoke with 200-250 people that day and thought, who gets to listen to this kind of feedback? I was reminded that I wasn't a bad guy who deserved to be put under investigation, scrutinized, bullied, and belittled. I wasn't what Joe portrayed me to be. I would like to think I am what I put out into the world. And if the feedback during my goodbyes were a true reflection of this, I thought to myself, "I'm okay."

I walked into the executive conference room before a meeting started. I said goodbye to my executive staff and thanked them for their knowledge and camaraderie. My message fell flat as they silently stared at the table. I wanted to go out on a high note. It wasn't in me to burn bridges. But damn, did I want to throw a match.

Not one person looked up to say goodbye.

Joe sat at the head of the table, silent and avoiding all eye contact.

Then I remembered that I owned the keys to *this* prison.

That was the last I ever saw of Joe.

EPILOGUE TO 'RELEASED FROM PRISON'

"Without justice there can be no peace. He who passively accepts evil is as much involved in it as he who helps perpetrate it."

— Martin Luther King, Jr.

WHAT DO YOU DO WHEN MULTIPLE allegations of workplace bullying, harassment, and retaliation are continually ignored, dismissed, or not investigated? For years, Joe received multiple allegations for the above issues. Yet, the heads of the organization have handled it in one of two ways, gas lighting the accuser or ignoring it altogether, leaving many poor victims traumatized, without jobs, or second guessing their experiences.

Over 41 staff signatures were collected on a formal "vote of no confidence" (VONC) letter and delivered to the top management, just to be denied. In addition, multiple high-level medical personnel quit for similar

Stalin-related reasons.

Since I left, two more people no longer work there; one quit, while the other was fired. In my conversations with many of them and reading the VONC, most people felt targeted in the same predictable style I experienced. Like most dictators, Joe didn't seem to stray from his methodology. To date, no one has been held accountable.

Stalin is still on the loose.

Shortly after leaving the prison, I started working for the local health department. As part of the orientation, I was required to watch multiple videos on workplace harassment. Surprisingly, I found myself tearing up, and realized I shared the same experience as the stories I just watched. I was floored. I thought, *if it could happen to me, it could happen to anyone.*

One can only hope that Joe will have his day of reckoning very soon.

To my friends, colleagues, and coworkers that experienced similar actions by Joe, I'm sorry that happened to you.

Dear Joe, karma's a bitch.

ONE LAST THING ...

"The moment you start to wonder if you deserve better, you do."

— Unknown

IN THE END, THIS BOOK IS ABOUT compassion. The lack of compassion from bureaucracies that see patients as revenue generators, and providers as their puppets. The abysmal lack of compassion from the insurance companies, who whittle humanity into codes and reimbursements. Compassion for our patients, which brings purpose to our job. Compassion for others, so we can make people feel like they aren't alone in this world. And self-compassion, so we aren't so hard on ourselves.

But I, too, fail at self-compassion and pretend everything is copacetic. Yet, wonder why I'm irritable, frustrated or that my nails are chewed down to the quick. It's because I am human that I fail at compassion. That I am human, is why I won't fail forever. We all share moments of apathy, misery, and sadness. But when we fail our patients because we couldn't find it within ourselves to show benevolence, it's time to take a step back and take inventory of ourselves. These moments of compassion don't need to be grand, just thoughtful. And if you're not sure what to do or say, think of what *you* would want in your moments of need.

In the bureaucratic milieu of medicine, I've realized that even when the rules change in the middle of the game, our fundamental   is the only stable entity. We can blame the system, HMOs, and lack of time for the care we deliver, but if compassion is our go-to, then I don't think our care should be affected significantly by things that are out of our control. I think that's why, despite all the mishegaas (Yiddish for craziness) around me, I still made heartfelt connections with my patients.

For patients:

You deserve to care for yourself. Not because you've earned it, but because you're terrific. You're alive! That alone deserves attention and compassion.

Though our healthcare system is complicated and messy, that shouldn't stop you from seeking the care you deserve. Suppose you're one of the lucky ones that receive insurance through your job, yet they only offer HMOs. Now what? Maybe you'll get lucky and have a warm provider that will see you when you need it. They exist; this book is a case in point. But if you're not so lucky, *maybe it's time to rethink how to make the system work for you.*

If you can sacrifice one Starbucks daily (I know that's asking a lot), and draw up the courage, you can change your life—just like the pinball. Most direct primary care (DPC) practices (like Willow) cost between $80-125 per person per month. So, if you can choose a higher deductible plan, paying less for your health insurance (to cover hospitalizations—catastrophic care), you can use those saved funds to afford a DPC doctor. Many times, it can be paid with a healthcare savings account (HSA), a nice incentive.

Maybe it's time to challenge the status quo.

For my healthcare comrades (brothers and sisters of war):

In reading this, I hope you took away one thing that will improve the quality of connections with your patients. Our patients deserve less from us, don't they? They deserve less judgment, less apathy, and less irritation. Even though the system bears down on us, we are the only ones that control how we react in this system. I understand that sometimes it feels like it's too much. Maybe you feel lost? Unsure of yourself? Want to quit? Run away and never turn back? Or quit medicine altogether? Instead, reflect on how incredible (and challenging) this job can be: Can you remember the first time you wanted to be a doctor or other healthcare provider? Can you remember the moment when your life changed? Can you remember how it felt when you received your acceptance into medical school? Or received your diploma? Can you remember how it felt putting on your short white coat for the first time? Can you remember what it was like to save a life? To lose a life? To tell a woman that she's not having a miscarriage, after all? To see a stillborn sitting amongst the trash in the supply room, waiting to be picked up but then delivering a healthy baby in the next room moments later? To be belittled by your attending but to be seen by another? To wish the day would be over or to be so excited that you can't wait for the next one to begin?

We are part of an exclusive club, aren't we? Not an elite one, just a unique one. One that gets the honor to share the darkest and brightest moments with our patients—in trust. It's communion. Not necessarily in the religious way, but in the way that it's most natural, *love.*

Or in the Hindu manner, which is my favorite—"Namasté" (nah-mas-tay): *My soul honors your soul. I honor the light, love, truth, and beauty within you because it is also within me.*

In sharing these things, we are the same; we are one.

Lastly, before you engage with a patient, please ask yourself, if this person was your mother (spouse, brother, sister, best friend, etc.), how would you treat them? Better yet, if that person was *you*, then how would you treat *you*?

Then, do that!

Namasté.

THE FINAL KISS

"Stress is caused by being 'here' but wanting to be 'there.'"

— Eckhart Tolle

I WOULD LIKE TO TAKE A MOMENT TO say a few things about an old friend who isn't with us anymore. You were my support in times of need. You helped guide me when I was lost. You showed me a path to follow in my life. Because of you I found love, enjoyment, purpose, success, and meaning. I also found sorrow, grief, and pain. But that's okay, my friend, because I knew you meant no harm. For your presence, I am grateful. For your demise, I am melancholy. I will take the lessons you've taught me and teach them to others. I've learned my lessons and have you to thank for them. If you were here right now, I would bow my head, place my hand on your shoulder, and whisper, rest in peace *healthcare system*, rest in peace. Then I would place one final kiss on your forehead.

Index of Stories
and Other Quips

23. Josefina and her culture: **I'm OK? You're OK?**
24. John and his erection: **I'm OK? You're OK?**
25. Tammy the ER nurse: **I'm OK? You're OK?**
26. Eleanor and her life insurance: **The Scarlet Letter**
27. Ken and his Maraca: **The Scarlet Letter**
28. Dana and her suicidal ideations: **The Scarlet Letter**
29. My deposition: **C.Y.A.**
30. On call Q2: **Would you like fries with that?**
31. Umm—The lunch and learn: **Lunch Meeting at Noon: Compassion 101**
32. Tina and her threatened miscarriage: **Do You Have It?**
33. Addiction Casino: **The Pain Merry-Go-Round?**
34. My separation: **Uncomfortable? Well, That's a Start.**
35. Barry and his chronic pain: **Three Is Your New Zero**
36. My four rules in prison: **A View Is Worth 1,000 Words**
37. Rectal retaliation: **"Toto, I've Got a Feeling We're not in Kansas Anymore."**
38. Mr. U. Penile pen insertion: **"Toto, I've Got a Feeling We're not in Kansas Anymore."**
39. Mrs. N. The Nurse practitioner and the shank: **"Toto, I've Got a Feeling We're not in Kansas Anymore."**
40. Mr. B and his walker: **"Toto, I've Got a Feeling We're not in Kansas Anymore."**
41. Mr. P's bright light: **"Toto, I've Got a Feeling We're not in Kansas Anymore."**
42. Joseph Stalin: **Released From Prison, Epilogue to Released From Prison**
43. Namaste: **One Last Thing**
44. The Eulogy: **The Final Kiss**

Acknowledgments

Writing a book is much more difficult than I ever imagined. Funny, it's not the writing or getting the ideas on the page that were the difficult part. The challenge was making my ideas clear for all readers. Many mornings Jenn and I slurped down coffee, put our feet up, and did *another* line edit, constantly challenging my fragile self-esteem. It's a very intimate process doing a detailed edit with your spouse. I experienced constant feelings that my writing *isn't good enough*, especially as we scratched out sections and reworked them over and over. Letting Jenn into my world was nothing new, but somehow, I kept finding my own walls to tear down, which made the process challenging. As she's edited before, she reminds me, "This is the process, Michael . . . and it's not easy for any author." There is nothing that provides as much comfort in this world as having the support of your partner. I am filled with gratitude. *(The statement on her coffee cup couldn't be more true—Best Wife Ever).*

There were some very important people in this book that left an impression on me, in perpetuity. For without them, I wouldn't have had the chance to grow, challenge myself and face some hard truths:

The ER doctor that kissed my Bubby, who taught me what true compassion looks like.

Dr. T, for *seeing* me.

The English Surgeon, who taught me what I didn't want to be.

Vasectomy surgeon, who gave me the insight to respect the patient, even during procedures.

Eleanor and Tammy who taught me to have foresight and be humble, respectively.

Joseph Stalin, who gave me another obstacle to overcome.

I must acknowledge:

My incredible daughter for giving me purpose. You are amazing, just as you are! I love you, angel.

My parents. Thank you for supporting me and

encouraging my creativity, always!

My Bubby Pauline. You are missed. Thank you for buying me my first stethoscope.

My parents (in-laws). I'm still married because of you. Thank you for all your encouragement.

My friends. Thank you for being supportive and wonderful and offering feedback (and legal counsel), when needed.

My Launch Team, who ironically, signed up for this shit: Stacey Dault, Matthew Mintz, MD, Karen, Michael Soto, Dr. Louise Ye-Liew, Jennifer Poptic, MD, FAAFP, Maksim Khokhlov, Dr. Charles Catania, Ronen Kleinman, Adam J.S. Frazier, Rod Louden, LMFT, Karen, Kristina Tetzlaff, Yusuf Mathai MD MPH, Jennie Coble, Sue Miranda, Leslie Goldstein, Dr. Brandon, Laura Poss, McEwan, James Adlhoch, RN, PHN, MA, MS, Dana Urick and everyone else in the launch team who isn't listed here.

Lastly, my wife, Jenn. You have incredible intestinal fortitude and patience. You always see the best in me. I know this was a challenging process for you, which I never underestimated. I really did appreciate each crossed-out paragraph, "Rework," or "Try this instead," suggestion that you wrote. Thank you, my love. You are my best friend. You can find her website here: www.jennifferlewisphd.com.

To Leave a Review, Contact the Author, or Learn More

Thank you for taking your valuable time to read this book. Please consider leaving a review at the online store where you purchased it.

If you would like to receive updates or join the mailing list:

www.michaellewismd.com

www.willowbaypress.com

or use your phone and scan the QR code(s) below:

Find me on Twitter

www.twitter.com/MichaelLewisMD

@MichaelLewisMD

Find me on Facebook

https://www.facebook.com/100084798513003

Notes

[1] "Adverse Childhood Experiences (ACEs): Preventing Early Trauma to Improve Adult Health." *Centers for Disease Control and Prevention.* https://www.cdc.gov/vitalsigns/aces.

[2] "Seinfeld The Soup Nazi (TV Episode 1995) – Plot Summary." *IMDb.* https://imdb.com/title/tt0697782/plotsummary.

[3] "18 Toughest Entrance Exams and Interviews in the World." *RankRed.* http://rankred.com/top-10-toughest-entrance-exams-in-the-world.

[4] "Paternalism in Medicine." *The LSU Medical and Public Health Law Site.* http://biotech.law.lsu.edu/map/PaternalisminMedicine.html.

[5] Beauchamp TL and JF Childress. *Principles of Biomedical Ethics.* Oxford: Oxford University Press, 2001.

[6] Charles, CA et al. "Shared Treatment Decision Making: What Does it Mean to Physicians?" *J Clin Oncol* 2003, 21: 932–936.

[7] Murray, Elizabeth et al. "Clinical Decision-Making: Patients' Preferences and Experiences." *Patient Educ Couns* 2007, 65: 189–196.

[8] Butow, PN et al. "The Dynamics of Change: Cancer Patients' Preferences for Information, Involvement, and Support." *Ann Oncol* 1997, 8: 857–863.7

Mazur DJ, et al. "Patients' Preferences for Risk Disclosure and Role in Decision Making for Invasive Medical Procedures. *J Gen Intern Med* 1997, 12: 114– 117.

[9] Schattner, A. "What Do Patients Really Want to Know?" *QJM* 2002, 95: 135–136.

[10] "Who Makes Medical Decisions in Texas if There Is no Medical Power of Attorney?" *Rania Combs Law.* https://raniacombslaw.com/resources/who-makes-medical-decisions-if-i-do-not-have-a-medical-power-of-attorney.

[11] "Are Quarantines Back?" *UCLA Department of Epidemiology.* http://www.ph.ucla.edu/epi/bioter/quarantinesback.html.

[12] Evidence-Based Medicine Working Group. "Evidence-Based Medicine: A New Approach to Teaching the Practice of Medicine." *JAMA* 1992, 268(17): 2420-5.

[13] Sackett, DL et al. "Evidence Based Medicine: What it Is and What it Isn't." *BMJ* 1996, 312(7023): 71–72.

[14] Nespor, Cassie. "19th Century Doctors in the U.S." *Melnick Medical Museum.* https://melnickmedicalmuseum.com/2009/03/11/19th-century-doctors-in-the-us.

[15] "Stories of Frontier Settlement Doctors." *OHSU Historical Collections and Archives.* http://ohsu.edu/xd/education/library/about/collections/historical-collections-archives/exhibits/frontier-settlement-doctors.cfm

[16] Boulton, Terynn. "'Blowing Smoke Up Your Ass' Used to Be Literal." *Gizmodo.* http://gizmodo.com/blowing-smoke-up-your-ass-used-to-be-literal-1578620709.

[17] Anglis, Jaclyn. "When 'Blowing Smoke Up Your Ass' Was Much More Than Just a Saying." *All That's Interesting.* https://allthatsinteresting.com/blowing-smoke-up-your-ass.

[18] Olaisen, R. Henry et al. "Assessing the Longitudinal Impact of Physician-Patient Relationship on Functional Health." *Annals of Family Medicine* September 2020, 18 (5): 422-29.

[19] "National Doctors' Day." *Wikipedia.* https://en.wikipedia.org/wiki/National_Doctors'_Day.

[20] Marques-Pinto, Alexandra et al. "Predictors of Burnout Among Physicians: Evidence From a National Study in Portugal" *Frontiers in Psychology,* 2021.

[21] "Medical Specialties With the Highest Burnout Rates." *AMA.* https://wire.ama-assn.org/life-career/medical-specialties-highest-burnout-rates.

[22] "2016 Survey of America's Physicians." *The Physicians Foundation.* https://physiciansfoundation.org/wp-content/uploads/2017/12/Biennial_Physician_Survey_2016.pdf.

[23] Peckham, Carol. "Medscape Malpractice Report 2015: Why Most Doctors Get Sued." *Medscape.* https://medscape.com/features/slideshow/public/malpractice-report-2015.

[24] Crane Mark. "Does 'Defensive' Medicine Differ From 'Careful' Medicine?" *Medscape.* http://www.medscape.com/viewarticle/838357_2.

[25] "America's Top States for Business 2016." *CNBC.* http://cnbc.com/2016/07/12/americas-top-states-for-business-2016-the-list-and-ranking.html.

[26] "Congress Must Act to Halt Medicare Payment Cuts and Avoid Further Damage to the U.S. Health-Care System." *American Academy of Audiology.* https://www.audiology.org/congress-must-act-to-halt-medicare-payment-cuts-and-avoid-further-damage-to-the-u-s-health-care-system.

[27] "DSM History." *American Psychiatric Association.* https://psychiatry.org/psychiatrists/practice/dsm/history-of-the-dsm.

[28] Brijnath, Bianca et al. "Trends in GP prescribing of psychotropic medications among young patients aged 16–24 years: a case study analysis." *BMC Psychiatry* 2017.

[29] Weed, Karen. "Top 10 Most Common HCC Codes." *RCxRules*. https://www.rcxrules.com/blog/common-hcc-codes.

[30] Adams, R., Boscarino, J., & Figley, C. (2006). "Compassion Fatigue and Psychological Distress Among Social Workers: A Validation Study." *American Journal of Orthopsychiatry, 76*(1), 103-108.

[31] Mannion, Russell. "Enabling Compassionate Healthcare: Perils, Prospects and Perspectives." *Int J Health Policy Manag.* 2014, 2(3): 115–117.

[32] Cocker, Fiona and Nerida Joss. "Compassion Fatigue among Healthcare, Emergency and Community Service Workers: A Systematic Review." *International Journal of Environmental Research and Public Health*. June 2016, 13(6): 618.

[33] Tolle, Eckhart. *The Power of Now*. London: Hodder Paperback, 2001.

[34] *Freedom Massage*. https://www.breakfree-massage.com/about.

[35] Davenport, Liam. "Mortality Increased With Long-Acting Opioids." *Medscape*. http://medscape.com/viewarticle/864985.

[36] Tettey, Naa-Solo, et al. "Purple Drank, Sizurp, and Lean: Hip-Hop Music and Codeine Use, A Call to Action for Public Health Educators." *The Canadian Center of Science and Education*. https://www.ccsenet.org/journal/index.php/ijps/article/view/0/42126.

[37] "Marketplace Plan Selections by Metal Level." *KFF*. https://www.kff.org/health-reform/state-indicator/ marketplace-plan-selections-by-metal-level-2.

[38] Lincoff, Nina. "The Future of Healthcare Could Be in Concierge Medicine." *Healthline*. http://healthline.com/health-news/the-future-of-healthcare-could-be-in-concierge-medicine-063015.

Made in United States
North Haven, CT
22 November 2022

27111881R00176